"Dr. Marschall's book would have saved me so much time and stress wher to figure out billing insurance companies and clinical documentation! This guide should be on the shelf of all mental health counseling students and new mental health professionals alike. I found the sample intake interviews and notes to be very helpful!"

Casey O'Brien Martin, LMHC, REAT, RN, *Author of* Skills for Big Feelings: A Guide for Teaching Kids Relaxation, Regulation, and Coping Techniques

"Regardless of population, documentation in the clinical world can be a challenging process to navigate. *Clinical Documentation with Children and Adolescents* by Dr. Amy Marschall, Psy.D., provides an articulate and comprehensive guide for the nuances in practice that must be approached specifically for child and adolescent clients. With thoughtful consideration of each step in the documentation process and excellent detailed templates and examples, this is a phenomenal resource for seasoned mental health professionals and is sure to become an essential addition to the library of any clinical student or new clinician who is interested in working with this population."

Andrea Dorn, MSW, LISW-CP, *Founder of Bloom Therapy and Wellness and Author of the* Mindful Steps Series™

"*Clinical Documentation for Children and Adolescents* is a must-read for any clinician working with this population. Dr. Marschall provides nuanced and detailed information to help any provider navigate the complexity of potential ethical and legal issues. This versatile manuscript will serve as a timeless guide for students as well as the most-seasoned clinicians."

Dr. Marina Harris, PhD, *Psychologist, CEO of Bloom Psychology Group*

CLINICAL DOCUMENTATION WITH CHILDREN AND ADOLESCENTS

This book addresses the unique challenges therapists face when documenting their clinical work with children, providing insight into what ethical, appropriate, and culturally competent practice looks like.

Clinical documentation is vital for ethical and legal practice, and good documentation helps clinicians leave room for client-centered and age-appropriate interventions, such as play therapy. Beginning with an overview of the important considerations unique to providers working with children, Amy Marschall offers guidance on all aspects of clinical documentation, such as intakes, treatment plans, mental status examinations, progress notes, safety plans, and more. Each chapter includes specific examples of clinical situations with guidance on how to document these situations effectively. With chapters on client confidentiality and telehealth, as well as special attention being paid to cultural awareness, including race, ethnicity, gender, sexual orientation, and socioeconomic status, this book includes blank templates of treatment plans, progress notes, and risk assessments for therapists to use in their practice.

This book is essential for any mental health professional who works with children in both individual and family work, including psychologists, licensed clinical social workers, licensed professional counselors, mental health counselors, marriage and family therapists, play therapists, school counselors, and therapist interns.

Amy Marschall, PsyD, is a licensed psychologist, speaker, and author, who lives in Sioux Falls, South Dakota, with her husband and two cats. Dr. Marschall specializes in child and adolescent mental healthcare and provides therapy and assessment through her private practice, RMH Therapy.

CLINICAL DOCUMENTATION WITH CHILDREN AND ADOLESCENTS

Treatment, Risks, and Ethics

Amy Marschall

Routledge
Taylor & Francis Group
NEW YORK AND LONDON

Designed cover image: © Flashvector / Getty Images

First published 2024
by Routledge
605 Third Avenue, New York, NY 10158

and by Routledge
4 Park Square, Milton Park, Abingdon, Oxon, OX14 4RN

Routledge is an imprint of the Taylor & Francis Group, an informa business

ISBN: 978-1-032-32733-4 (hbk)
ISBN: 978-1-032-32731-0 (pbk)
ISBN: 978-1-003-31644-2 (ebk)

DOI: 10.4324/9781003316442

Typeset in Stone Serif
by Apex CoVantage, LLC

CONTENTS

CHAPTER 1

OVERVIEW OF CLINICAL DOCUMENTATION FOR CHILDREN AND ADOLESCENTS

Clinical documentation is complex with a variety of requirements, and it seems to never end. You must note the specifics of the appointment, including clinical justification for interventions, client mental status and progress, safety, and the specifics of what occurred, as well as documentation of communication in between sessions, consultations, treatment plans, et cetera. When the client is a minor, what special considerations must be kept in mind concerning clinical documentation?

Clinical documentation is pervasive in therapy practice. We document everything we do, when we did it, who was present, and why. A common theme taught in graduate training is: "If you don't document it, it didn't happen."

While there are universal components to good clinical documentation, such as specific interventions used, changes in symptoms, and plans for follow up, best practice looks different when clients are minors, and the nuances of accurate notes that protect client confidentiality change significantly when you work with these populations. Ethical considerations look different when a client is underage and has a parent or legal guardian in charge of their care and medical considerations.

Special Considerations With Children and Adolescents

This section reviews various aspects of care and documentation that must be considered when working with children and adolescents, including what to keep in mind and why each aspect is important for providing ethical and competent care. These aspects are addressed in each chapter of this book.

Cultural Considerations

Regardless of the age range a therapist works with, they have an ethical obligation to be culturally competent and informed (Hays, 2009). This is, of course, an area in which each clinician continues to develop and grow throughout their career, not a course we take with a set end point at which we are "done."

When working with children, these considerations include understanding how the client and their family's cultural background informs their perception of what therapy is and what treatment looks like (Schwab-Stone et al., 2001). This can also impact how the child interacts with the therapist as an authority figure or as a stranger, as well as the parent's perception of what topics are appropriate to discuss in front of the client or what information shared in session is expected to be shared with the parent or guardian.

DOI: 10.4324/9781003316442-1

Individual family values should not be pathologized, but the predominantly white, Western-oriented field of mental health continues to do this. Clients from collectivist cultures have shared with me many times that previous therapists had described family dynamics as "enmeshed" and labeled the level of connection and involvement in each other's lives as pathological when it simply reflects their cultural values. This is not to say that families in collectivist cultures cannot have dysfunctional dynamics, but we as providers need to explore whether the dynamic is causing problems or if it is simply different from the therapist's preconceived notions about "healthy" relationships.

Clients in foster care or who have been adopted by caregivers of a different culture face specific identity issues that might not be prevalent in other cases (Mulkerns & Owen, 2008), including diffusion or uncertainty about their cultural identity. If the adoptive parents do not fully understand the child's culture, they might misinterpret behavior as disrespectful, rude, or oppositional due to miscommunication. They may also fail to maintain the child's connection to their culture of origin. In addition, if the foster family does not share the foster child's cultural identity, the child is at even higher risk for trauma or identity concerns later in life (Tyrell et al., 2019). The therapist must be aware of this when documenting information provided by the parents.

If the therapist is of a different cultural background than their client, they must be especially mindful of projecting their values onto the client. This is particularly true if the therapist is part of the dominant culture (for example, in the United States, a white therapist who is not an immigrant) (Ertl et al., 2019). Be mindful of how you describe the client's behaviors and symptoms through a neutral, therapeutic, and non-judgmental lens.

Developmentally Appropriate Assessment and Diagnosing

Children are not smaller adults. The way that they think, perceive the world around them, communicate, and interact are distinctly different from adults, and the variation among ages and developmental levels is huge. Their brains are growing, particularly the frontal lobe, impacting their ability to regulate their impulses, communicate, and process emotions.

Some assessments cannot be administered prior to a certain age, or different variations of the assessment are used for younger clients. For instance, the Millon Multiaxial Clinical Inventory is a personality measure used in adults age 18 and older (Millon et al., 2015). However, clients age 13 through 17 can take the Millon Adolescent Clinical Inventory (Millon et al., 2020), and those ages 9 through 12 can take the Millon Pre-Adolescent Clinical Inventory to gather information about their current mental health symptoms (Millon et al., 2005). The language used in the questions presented is tailored to these various ages, and the resulting scores are based on a normative population for each age. (There are, of course, limitations to this measure, particularly in light of the cultural considerations noted.)

Even if you do not use normative measures like the MCMI in your practice, assessing for whether a client's anxiety symptoms are typical or clinically significant will vary based on the client's age. The questions you ask must be tailored to the client's ability to understand their symptoms and provide insight into their experience. In addition, insight from parents, other guardians, or teachers can shed light on the client's specific symptoms, but the weight given to external sources of information will depend on the client's ability to provide information about their own experience.

Furthermore, many diagnoses in the *Diagnostic and Statistical Manual of Mental Disorders* cannot be assigned to people below a certain age due to developmental considerations (American Psychiatric Association, 2022). For example, some developmental disorders are not diagnosed prior to age five because there is a wide range of "typical development." Certain behaviors are developmentally appropriate when the client is five years old but may seem atypical or concerning when the client is 10. Similarly, some personality disorders cannot be diagnosed in adolescence due to the impact of hormones and frontal lobe development on behavior and relationships. When assessing minor clients, therapists and other mental health providers must understand which diagnoses are appropriate and why.

Developmentally Appropriate

The interventions used with a client should be determined based on what is the best fit for their unique needs, symptoms, and level of development. However, many providers must justify to payers (in the United States, this is often an insurance company) how a specific intervention is helpful, "evidence-based," and fits with an overarching treatment plan with measurable goals.

Additionally, many "evidence-based" interventions emphasize a rigid and structured approach to treatment that is not a good fit for many children. Following these interventions "correctly" can trigger power struggles or oppositionality with children who are nervous or simply do not want to follow the instructions presented (Norcross & Wampold, 2018). As such, it is often appropriate to deviate from the specific intervention, but this deviation must then be documented appropriately.

While it is important and ethical to utilize interventions that you believe will benefit your client, these interventions look different in preschool children, elementary-aged children, middle schoolers, high schoolers, and adults. With young children, it can be challenging to document age-appropriate, helpful interventions in a way that adequately explains the therapeutic benefit. Providers must also meet payer standards for documentation while making the client's needs their first priority in the treatment itself.

The challenge this presents to the therapist is keeping accurate documentation that reflects the care provided, using language that does not easily encompass what occurred in the session. How do you tailor interventions to the child's developmental level and then document this intervention following best practice and ethical guidelines?

Rapport Building

Relationship is the foundation for therapeutic change (Karver et al., 2006). We know that the connection between therapist and client, the indefinable "fit," the trust and safety of that relationship is the most important piece of therapy and growth. As such, any activity that builds rapport with your client is therapeutic and appropriate.

While this does not mean that therapy should consist *only* of rapport-building activities, an emphasis on building rapport is essential, especially early in treatment. Children especially need this focus on rapport for a few reasons. First, it is usually not the child's choice to come to therapy, so they might feel like they lack control in the situation, which can foster distrust with the therapist. This is particularly common in teens who start therapy at a parent or guardian's request. Second, parents and guardians teach children not to talk to strangers. When a child first comes for therapy, the therapist is a stranger. The therapist has to earn trust and build a relationship before the child can even begin to engage.

It can be challenging to justify these interventions to payers, even though rapport is essential before any additional work can take place. In my own clinical experience, rapport building can take several sessions, even months if the client has difficulty trusting adults due to past trauma. Even after the early rapport-building phase of therapy has finished, maintaining rapport is essential for continued progress in therapy. If a client takes a break from treatment due to a vacation, if there is a rupture in the therapeutic relationship, or if the child goes through a particularly difficult time, they might benefit from sessions focused on rapport rather than other therapeutic goals. Even if therapy progresses in a "typical" manner, if the focus of all subsequent sessions is on "interventions" with no room for rapport, the child might become defensive or less interested in engaging in treatment.

Often, rapport building includes engaging in activities chosen by the client. This can mean doing coloring pages together, playing a board or card game without a therapeutic "take," or simply talking about the client's interests. When a session (or several sessions in a row) specifically emphasizes rapport building and no other treatment goals or therapeutic interventions, this must be documented appropriately.

Additionally, activities that build rapport can simultaneously be an intervention focused on another therapeutic goal. A child might enjoy playing a card game with the therapist, and the game might build rapport. At the same time, the child and therapist can practice frustration tolerance skills in the session when the child loses a hand or has to draw cards. The child can build impulse control by waiting their turn and executive functioning by deciding which card to play next based on the available options. You can note that an intervention worked for rapport as well as these other interventions simultaneously.

Documenting Play

Children communicate and process emotion through play because their brains are developmentally different from adult brains (Gil, 2012). In the same way that adults might talk through an emotionally difficult situation, children work through many things through imaginative and non-directive play. Play therapy sessions involve toys and activities seen in typical play, even though the mechanisms of play therapy differ from "just playing." While we know this can help with improving emotional well-being, play does not always "look" therapeutic. Not only that, but since play therapy does not always involve talking about anything specific, the therapist might not know the specific therapeutic benefit of a given moment of play (Parker et al., 2021).

In addition, play can be an important component of assessment and mental status evaluations because young children might struggle to answer specific questions testing for things like memory, orientation, or focus. However, they may be able to demonstrate these skills (or demonstrate ways they are lacking a skill) through play (Sarah et al., 2021). The toys and games a child selects and the way that they decide to interact with these items can be very telling of their emotional state, interests, and needs.

Play therapy can present challenges in documentation when justifying why this method was used and how it benefitted the client in a given session. Accurately capturing what occurred in session without making assumptions, jumping to conclusions, or projecting meaning inappropriately onto the play is difficult. At the same time, documentation of a play session must capture the clinical value of the session.

Confidentiality

Laws about confidentiality vary by jurisdiction. In the United States, components of a client's chart cannot be released unless the client signs an appropriate release of information (Health Insurance Portability and Accountability Act [HIPAA] of 1996, Pub. L. No. 104–191). However, when working in collaboration with a treatment team (such as other staff in an inpatient setting or with teachers or other individuals in a child's school system), therapists might be expected to share some information about treatment. This might be required for continuity of care with different services (medication management, occupational or speech therapy, creating and maintaining an appropriate Individual Education Plan). You must be able to communicate necessary and important information while maintaining client privacy and confidentiality.

Judges can order a therapist to turn notes over to the court or to lawyers, and although a therapist can contest this, they might be compelled to comply or face jail time. This can occur if a parent or guardian is charged with abuse, if the child becomes involved in the legal system, or if the child is in foster care. In addition, a parent's lawyer might ask a judge to order that records be released as part of a custody battle. We must keep in mind the possibility that someone else will legally and ethically gain access to a client's chart and document appropriately with their confidentiality in mind.

Insurance companies receive limited information about each session in order for a therapist to qualify for reimbursement. Although this does not typically include all the information detailed in notes, state insurance in the United States (Medicaid) and many private insurance companies routinely conduct chart audits to ensure that the therapist is providing proper care. These audits include requests for assessment reports, specific progress notes, or even the client's full chart. In these situations, a client might not have the option to ask the therapist not to comply with this request. Additionally, private insurance companies will sometimes indicate that they cannot process a claim unless the "full record" is submitted.

In addition to these confidentiality limitations, many jurisdictions allow parents or guardians to view minor clients' charts at any time or upon request. A therapist might have grounds to try to deny a request from a parent or guardian citing the client's well-being, but this is not always permitted by law.

If a minor client shares details with the therapist that are later released, this can destroy the therapeutic relationship. How can the client trust their therapist in the future if they know that information disclosed might be passed onto a parent, teacher, or someone else without the client's permission?

If a minor client comes out to their therapist as LGBTQ+ and feels that it is unsafe to be out to their parents for any reason, the therapist has an ethical duty to protect that client from harm by keeping this information confidential. If the parent obtains records and abuses the client as a result of what they learn, the therapist has failed in their obligation to keep the client safe.

While there is always risk that a third party might legally gain access to client records (treatment team members, insurance companies, or the court in legal cases), these risks increase for minors because a parent or guardian is a third party who can often easily gain access to the records. The parent or guardian might also consent to releasing records on the child's behalf.

When completing clinical documentation with a minor client, a therapist must be aware of possible confidentiality limitations while appropriately documenting session details. This balance is an important skill in providing ethical care.

Access to Records

Clinicians do not always share every aspect of their documentation and clinical record with a client directly, but sometimes clients request to view their chart or to access their records for various reasons, including applying for benefits or services, enlisting in the military, or for continuity of care with a new provider. Some providers do not share the chart with the client upon request due to concerns that reading the chart could be harmful, but current laws indicate that it is an adult client's right to see their records in almost all cases. We might not show a child their record since the child may not understand the concept of "progress notes" or a "treatment plan," or we might share details that are developmentally appropriate rather than the entire record.

At the same time, we often forget that a child eventually grows into an adult who will have the right to request their chart. HIPAA requires that we maintain records for seven years or three years after the client's eighteenth birthday, whichever length of time is longer, and clients can request records from their childhood once they reach the age of majority. As such, when documenting, imagine the child years from now reading what was written about them.

Aspects of Clinical Documentation

There are so many things to keep in mind with clinical documentation with minors, but fortunately, this book exists to talk you through each component of your documentation to ensure ethical best practice. Each of the following chapters explores the nuance and best practices for clinical documentation with minor clients.

Informed Consent

In most cases, if the client is a minor, their parent or guardian must provide consent for services. Some states have different laws around ages of consent for medical or mental health services. Regardless of whether the client themselves or their legal guardian is consenting to services, you need to address with your client that they are receiving mental healthcare and discuss this with them at a level that is developmentally appropriate. You must also discuss what exactly treatment looks like and how you handle issues like risk assessment and confidentiality with the legal guardian and the client. Consent issues are addressed in Chapter 2 of this book.

Billing Insurance

If you plan to bill insurance, you must be aware of which codes to use and what information is provided to the insurance company. Though this does not differ significantly with minors compared to adult clients, you will need to make sure you note who the policy holder is (if different from the client) and ensure that you use accurate billing codes. This will be discussed in Chapter 3.

Intake Interviews

When most adults present for mental health services, they come by themselves. Therapy intakes for individuals generally consist of just that individual meeting with the therapist unless they have a legal guardian due to a specific vulnerable adult status. With minor clients, your intake interview will most likely include information from individuals other than the client. With very young clients, the information gathered directly from the client will likely be limited due to the client's developmental level.

What does this look like in documenting intake interviews? What information is important to include, and what questions can help you get that information directly from the client, from a guardian, or from another available source? When getting information from multiple sources, how should your documentation present contradictory or conflicting information? What does a thorough developmental history look like? How can you best present the information gathered in the client's chart? This is addressed in Chapter 4.

Diagnoses

As noted, many diagnoses have age criteria. The client might have to be above or below a certain age to meet criteria, and this information will have to be updated regularly as the client develops or as new symptoms emerge or resolve. Therapists need to thoroughly document symptoms and justify which diagnosis or diagnoses is made as well as rule-outs, provisional diagnoses, or previous diagnoses that the client does not presently meet criteria for. Chapter 5 of this book details considerations around diagnosis with children and adolescents.

Treatment Plans

As with intake interviews, treatment plans for minor clients are distinct from most individual adult clients because multiple people have opinions about what the client's goals for therapy ought to be. While a therapist might have input about appropriate goals for effective treatment, they will be working with parents/guardians as well as the client themselves in creating the treatment plan. At times, input from the school district or other providers might also be important to consider.

How do you balance the client's priorities with the parent or guardian's stated goals for treatment? How do you document treatment goals and interventions in accordance with ethical and billing requirements? What can you document if the client's stated goal for treatment is something like, "To not have to come to therapy anymore?" How can you help clients and guardians articulate specific and measurable goals when they present vague reasons for coming to therapy? Chapter 6 delves into treatment plans.

Mental Status Examinations

Many standard questions included in a mental status examination are either not suitable or confusing for young clients. For instance, it is not exactly developmentally appropriate to ask a four-year-old about a news story that they saw recently.

What does a mental status examination look like in preschool-age children? Elementary? Middle school? Adolescents? How do you observe and assess symptoms in those who are too young to provide reliable verbal answers to questions or those who are nervous or reluctant to share? How do you interpret behaviors in a mental status examination without making assumptions about the client? This is covered in Chapter 7.

Progress Notes

It is particularly challenging to craft progress notes that are thorough and accurate, and to maintain confidentiality concerns detailed earlier in this chapter. Notes must also detail specifics of the session as well as justification for the interventions used or not used. You need to tie in the client's treatment goals, how they were addressed or why they were put on hold for that session, and how the client has progressed, regressed, or stayed the same. Any changes in symptom presentation, new symptoms, or changes in diagnosis must also be indicated.

Therapists spend more documentation time on progress notes than any other area. We need thorough notes that capture session details in an efficient manner. Chapter 8 discusses all things related to progress notes.

Consultation/Contact Notes

There is always the possibility that a therapist will have contact with a client outside of their scheduled session. For many adult clients, this can consist of the client asking a question or providing an update between sessions. Unless you have an appropriate release on file, it is usually not appropriate to respond to contacts from someone other than the client (Health Insurance Portability and Accountability Act [HIPAA] of 1996, Pub. L. No. 104–191). (Of course, mandated reporting, concerns about harm to self or others, and court orders are exceptions to this rule.)

As a licensed mental health provider, you also have an ethical responsibility to seek appropriate consultation or supervision when appropriate. If you feel "stuck" or need guidance on appropriate interventions, next steps in treatment, or how to handle an ethical concern, it is necessary and appropriate to seek consultation from a fellow provider. Typically, these consultations do not include sharing identifying client information (American Psychological Association, 2017). However, you still need to document in the client's chart the reason for the consultation as well as the content.

With child and teen clients, their parent or guardian may contact you in between sessions with questions about treatment, updates about symptoms, or safety concerns. Many guardians authorize other care professionals, teachers, school counselors, et cetera, to contact the primary therapist. These contacts must be documented appropriately and include the reason for the contact, why they reached out, and what information you disclosed.

Maintaining the client's confidentiality while sharing helpful information is an important balance. All contacts regarding the client's treatment should be included in their chart. This is addressed in Chapter 9.

Safety and Risk Assessments

Many therapists experience anxiety and nervousness around risk assessments and safety planning. This makes sense – your first job is to keep your clients safe, and knowing they might not be safe can be terrifying. Safety concerns often fall under a confidentiality limitation, so determining the best way to document and communicate this concern to guardians is important. You want to maintain your client's trust while ensuring that they have the care and support that they need.

Much practice and training around safety planning focuses on "safety contracts," but these have been shown to be ineffective in preventing suicide (Dueweke & Bridges, 2018). Similarly, some providers err on the side of caution by hospitalizing as soon as a client brings up suicidal ideation, even if they do not have plan or intent to act on these thoughts. Unnecessary hospitalization can be stressful if not traumatic and can exacerbate symptoms, as well as reducing trust with the therapist (Cusack et al., 2003).

How can you assess for safety effectively, without over- or under-intervening? What questions should you ask to determine the client's level of risk? How do you document that the risk is present along with justification for how you handled the risk? Chapter 10 of this book focuses on risk assessment.

Letters

Clients or their guardians might request letters for a variety of reasons, including to verify attendance at sessions or to provide information that will be used in court. This can be challenging for therapists to navigate, as we want to maintain confidentiality, stay in our lane and scope of practice, and help the client or their guardian where appropriate.

What should be included in a letter? What should be left out? What is the minimum information that you need to include without violating privacy? When is it important to say no? This is addressed in Chapter 11, the final chapter of this book.

How to Use This Book

While the primary focus of this book is documentation with minor clients, it includes valuable information about clinical skills, such as questions to ask in specific situations and considerations when formulating a diagnosis. In conjunction with other resources and appropriate clinical training, its goal is to prepare you for clinical work with children, teens, and their families.

Each chapter includes templates of various note forms, including intakes, treatment plans, progress notes, and contact notes. Different options are included for each, and you are encouraged to try different things to see what is the best fit for your style. All options included should be acceptable in most clinical settings, but always check with any director or supervisor who oversees your work to ensure that they meet your organization's specific standards.

If a particular template is a good fit, you are welcome to duplicate it for your clinical work. You can also take a template and make modifications so that it fits your preferences and needs. Add sections that work for you or remove parts that do not apply. Since mental health treatment is so individualized, developing the tools to create something unique for each client's needs is more important than finding the perfect template to fit into any situation.

It is my hope that this book can guide you in what many therapists refer to as the most tedious part of practice: Documentation.

Glossary of Terms

confidentiality: In mental health, confidentiality refers to the ethical requirement that providers limit disclosure of identifying client information, including their identity, diagnosis, treatment, assessment, progress, and any other information related to treatment.

culture: The specific values, beliefs, customs, language, and knowledge of a specific community or group.

development: The process of growth throughout the lifespan.

developmentally appropriate: Interventions or practices that promote a child's ongoing development by focusing on their current knowledge and abilities.

documentation: Any part of a client's record, relating to communications, treatment, interventions, payment, et cetera.

ethical: Practices that are in keeping with one's licensing ethics code.

ethics: Principles and guidelines that guide a provider's choices and behavior in their work.

evidence-based: An approach to treatment that emphasizes interventions with research backing demonstrating their effectiveness.

fit: The client's connection to the therapist and feeling that they "click" and agree on treatment plans, goals, and interventions.

intervention: Any technique, strategy, or activity intended to address or treat presenting symptoms.

minor: A client who has not reached the age of majority; in the United States, anyone who is under age 18 years.

non-directive play: An approach to play in which the child takes the lead and directs the session with the therapist following their guidance rather than dictating the direction of the session.

oppositionality: Refusing to comply or follow instructions.

play therapy: A type of therapy utilizing play activities to allow children to process emotional issues and mental health symptoms through play.

rapport: A positive, connected relationship between the client and therapist, often manifested by feelings of trust.

symptoms: In mental health, any behavior, emotion, or functional issue that is linked to psychological pathology or a mental health diagnosis.

typical: Expected.

Works Cited

American Psychological Association. (2017). *Ethical principles of psychologists and code of conduct (2002, amended effective June 1, 2010, and January 1, 2017).* www.apa.org/ethics/code/

American Psychiatric Association. (2022). *Diagnostic and statistical manual of mental disorders* (5th ed., Text Revision).

Cusack, K. J., Frueh, B. C., Hiers, T., Suffoletta-Maierle, S., & Bennett, S. (2003). Trauma within the psychiatric setting: A preliminary empirical report. *Administration and Policy in Mental Health and Mental Health Services Research, 30*(5), 453–460.

Dueweke, A. R., & Bridges, A. J. (2018). Suicide interventions in primary care: A selective review of the evidence. *Families, Systems, & Health, 36*(3), 289.

Ertl, M. M., Mann-Saumier, M., Martin, R. A., Graves, D. F., & Altarriba, J. (2019). The impossibility of client – therapist "match": Implications and future directions for multicultural competency. *Journal of Mental Health Counseling, 41*(4), 312–326. https://doi.org/10.17744/mehc.41.4.03

Gil, E. (2012). *The healing power of play: Working with abused children.* Guilford Press.

Hays, P. A. (2009). Integrating evidence-based practice, cognitive – behavior therapy, and multicultural therapy: Ten steps for culturally competent practice. *Professional Psychology: Research and Practice, 40*(4), 354–360. https://doi.org/10.1037/a0016250

Health Insurance Portability and Accountability Act. Pub. L. No. 104–191, § 264, 110 Stat. (1936). https://uslaw.link/citation/us-law/public/104/191

Karver, M., Handelsman, J., Fields, S., & Bickman, L. (2006). Meta-analysis of therapeutic relationship variables in youth and family therapy: The evidence for different relationship variables in the child and adolescent treatment outcome literature. *Clinical Psychology Review, 26*(1), 50–65. https://doi.org/10.1016/j.cpr.2005.09.001

Millon, T., Grossman, S., & Millon, C. (2015). *Millon multiaxial clinical inventory* (4th ed., Evaluation). Pearson Assessments.

Millon, T., Tringone, R., Grossman, S., & Millon, C. (2020). *Millon adolescent clinical inventory-II* (Evaluation). Pearson Assessments.

Millon, T., Tringone, R., Millon, C., & Grossman, S. (2005). *Millon pre-adolescent clinical inventory* (Evaluation). Pearson Assessments.

Mulkerns, H., & Owen, C. (2008). Identity development in emancipated young adults following foster care. *Smith College Studies in Social Work, 78*(4), 427–449.

Norcross, J. C., & Wampold, B. E. (2018). A new therapy for each patient: Evidence-based relationships and responsiveness: NORCROSS and WAMPOLD. *Journal of Clinical Psychology, 74*(11), 1889–1906. https://doi.org/10.1002/jclp.22678

Parker, M. M., Hergenrather, K., Smelser, Q., & Kelly, C. T. (2021). Exploring child-centered play therapy and trauma: A systematic review of literature. *International Journal of Play Therapy, 30*(1), 2.

Sarah, B., Parson, J., Renshaw, K., & Stagnitti, K. (2021). Can children's play themes be assessed to inform play therapy practice? *Clinical Child Psychology and Psychiatry, 26*(1), 257–267.

Schwab-Stone, M., Ruchkin, V., Vermeiren, R., & Leckman, P. (2001). Cultural considerations in the treatment of children and adolescents. *Child and Adolescent Psychiatric Clinics of North America, 10*(4), 729–743. https://doi.org/10.1016/S1056-4993(18)30027-0

Tyrell, F. A., Marcelo, A. K., Trang, D. T., & Yates, T. M. (2019). Prospective associations between trauma, placement disruption, and ethnic-racial identity among newly emancipated foster youth. *Journal of Adolescence, 76*, 88–98.

CHAPTER 2

INFORMED CONSENT AND OTHER PAPERWORK

As healthcare providers, we are legally obligated to obtain informed consent from every client. In the case of children and adolescents, we typically need to get this consent from the legal guardian, but they are not our client. This chapter digs into best practices for informed consent and assent when your client is under 18.

Consent and Agreement Paperwork

When I was a college student, I heard somewhere that "choosing a career is deciding what kind of paperwork you want to do for the rest of your life." This is undeniably true for mental health professionals. Before we even meet a client, we have to complete extensive paperwork about consenting to treatment, collecting payment, and understanding office policies.

You might also have forms for your client, their guardian, or both to complete prior to the intake to give you a starting point for questions to ask during the diagnostic interview (discussed in Chapter 4) or to get some general background information to save time during that intake.

Much of the consent paperwork involves the legal guardian or guardians reading and acknowledging various policies. Of course, we must still review these policies with the client to ensure they understand what they signed. They may come to us with questions about these forms. It is not enough to have a signature; we have an obligation to make sure that the legal guardian understands what they are agreeing to and can ask any questions they have.

You might update your paperwork as your practice changes or if a new law requires an update. In this case, existing clients will need to review and sign new consent paperwork. Additionally, depending on your jurisdiction, you might be required to get updated consent after a certain amount of time has passed. For instance, you may be required to get updated written consent every 12 months.

Consent Versus Assent

Providers are ethically and legally obligated to obtain informed consent from clients or their guardians before providing services. This means that they must have information about risks, benefits, procedures, limitations, and other relevant information about the service that will be provided. Assent is simply agreement to participate in treatment.

With minor clients, the parent or legal guardian must provide written consent unless the client is old enough to provide consent themselves. Even if the guardian provides consent, the client can provide assent or indicate that they agree to receive services. Assent does not have to be in writing, but written consent is typically legally required.

DOI: 10.4324/9781003316442-2

There might be situations where a client does not assent to services that the guardian consented to. You may then use your professional judgment to determine next steps: If the client does not want to attend therapy, is it in their best interest for you to decline to continue seeing them? Are they potentially unsafe due to suicidal ideation or risky behaviors, and for their safety they need monitoring? Are they willing to try to establish rapport and see whether they might be open to therapy in the future? Document your decision and the reason behind it in the intake note (see more about this in Chapter 4).

Legal Obligations

Always check your jurisdiction for specific requirements. Typically, informed consent documentation includes information about privacy policies, fees, and the type of service that will be provided. You additionally need written consent to bill a client's insurance.

Joint Custody

When a minor client has parents who are not together, providers must follow specific laws regarding who needs to give consent to treatment. This can vary by jurisdiction. For example, in South Dakota, if the parents were never married, the mother has full custody of the child by default unless the family has a custody agreement signed by a judge indicating otherwise.

If one parent has full custody, that parent may sign consent for treatment, and no additional signatures are needed. However, if the parents have joint custody, the provider needs to reach out to both parents and attempt to obtain consent. Ideally, both parents should sign the consent paperwork.

That being said, sometimes a parent has joint custody but is not involved in their child's life or care, or you are unable to contact them. Some parents do not exercise visitation rights or stay in touch with their child even if they have the legal right to do so. In this case, the child will never receive treatment if you have to wait until you can track down the other parent before you can see them. If you are unable to reach the other parent to confirm whether or not they consent to treatment, you may document that you attempted to reach them and did not hear back, then move forward with only one parent's signature.

If an uninvolved parent answers when you call and verbally indicates that they will sign the consent paperwork but then does not respond or follow up, you may be able to document their verbal consent and move forward.

If the other parent responds and states that they do not consent to treatment, you cannot move forward with treating the child unless that parent consents or a judge orders treatment. In the event that a minor is court ordered to see a therapist, the therapist can move forward with treatment upon receipt of the signed court order.

Depending on the jurisdiction's age of medical consent, a child might be able to provide their own consent to treatment.

Ages of Medical Consent

In most places, a client is considered an adult when they turn 18 years old. This is true for most of the United States and Europe as well as many other countries, though in some countries the age is 19, 20, or 21 (OECD Family Database, 2016). In Mississippi, the age of majority (adulthood) used to be 21 but was lowered to 18 in 2021 (Senate Bill 2355, 2021). In Nebraska, the age of majority is 19 for legal independence from one's parents, but at age 18 individuals can make their own medical decisions (Marvin and Virginia Schmid Law-Related Education Endowment, 2011). Alabama has a similar law, indicating

19 as the legal age of majority but granting certain rights at age 18 (Age of Majority Designated as 19 Years, AL Code § 26–1–1, 2018). Always be familiar with local laws where you are licensed to practice. If you are licensed in multiple jurisdictions, it can be helpful to keep a spreadsheet.

Not only does the age of majority for becoming an adult vary, but the age at which an individual can consent to medical and mental health care is often different. For example, in Alabama, although an individual is not fully a legal adult until age 19, a 14-year-old can consent to medical care (When a Minor May Give Consent Generally, AL Code §§22–8–4; 22–8–7, 2013). In Alaska, an individual can consent to medical care if they are living independently from their parents, regardless of age (Examination and treatment of Minors, AK Code §25–20–025, 2016). In South Carolina, there is no minimum age at which a client can seek medical services without parental consent as long as the provider believes that "such services are deemed necessary" (SC Code §65–5–350, 2019).

Basically, medical consent is complicated. If a minor contacts a therapist, and laws in that jurisdiction allow them to consent to medical treatment, the therapist may see the client with just the client's consent to treatment. The minor has the right in these instances to confidentiality of their medical record, including from the parent or guardian, without authorization to release information or an order from a judge. However, if the client is on their parents' insurance and needs to use insurance to cover the cost of services, be aware that the insurance company will likely mail an explanation of benefits to the policy holder, usually the parent. This will be discussed further in the next chapter.

If the client's parents are divorced and share custody, a child who is at the age of medical consent can authorize their care without informing the other parent if the child requests this. For example, if the client's father brings them for therapy, and the client states, "I don't want Mom to know," you can usually proceed with signatures from the father and client. Of course, always consult your malpractice attorney to ensure that you are following all laws applicable to your jurisdiction.

Additionally, if you work with teenagers, you might experience clients starting therapy as minors and reaching the age of majority during their treatment. In this case, they will have to complete their own consent paperwork and authorizations after they reach this age. They should already have knowledge about what they are consenting to as part of the assent process, but they might have additional questions as they review the paperwork in full. In addition, if their parent is still paying their co-pays or session fees, you will need a release of information to send bills to the parent rather than to the adult client.

Depending on the nature of treatment, if the client wants you to provide information about their treatment to the parent, you will need this spelled out in the release of information as well. If you have been sharing information about treatment with the parent, and the client becomes an adult and declines to sign a release of information, you will have to discontinue this practice immediately.

This conversation should start prior to the client's birthday so that they, their parent, and you are prepared for any shifts in treatment, privacy, et cetera, when they become an adult.

Registration Paperwork

Registration paperwork incudes demographic and contact information that you need to know about a client in order to create their chart. You might decide to have a long, thorough registration form, which can give extensive background information about the client, or you can have something more brief that just gives you the basics about their case and what they need. Longer forms are more comprehensive and provide you with more details before the intake session, but they are a bigger demand on the client's time prior to the session. Guardians who struggle with executive dysfunction or organization might have difficulty completing a long form or become overwhelmed.

The important pieces of information to gather are basic identifying information, including name and date of birth, as well as any relevant custody information, address and phone number, and at least some basic information about why they are seeking services.

Developmental History Form

Depending on why the guardian is seeking services for the client, they might be primarily focused on the presenting issue. However, therapists need background information and history in addition to the current issues that bring the client for treatment. Some providers choose to collect information through a developmental history form as part of their consent and registration paperwork to free up time and energy during the intake interview. This information can additionally guide questioning during the intake.

Like the registration form, a developmental history form can be brief or long, depending on how thorough you prefer to be prior to the intake. Again, a brief developmental history form only gives basic information, but an extensive form that is several pages long might overwhelm parents.

In cases where the parents are not together, it can be beneficial to get two separate developmental history forms, as the parents may remember different relevant details. This can allow more thorough background information. Since this form is informative and not a legal consent document, though, it is optional to get input from both – if one parent did not meet the child the first several years of the child's life, they might not have first-hand knowledge of early developmental milestones, illnesses, or behaviors.

If the child is adopted or in foster care, and biological family is not known, not available, or not permitted to participate in the intake, limited information might be available. It can be helpful to let the guardian know that they can skip or indicate "not known" on sections as needed.

Therapy Agreement/Consent to Treatment

Something I have frequently said to parents is, "You would think that requesting an appointment implies that you consent to the appointment, but I have to get that in writing." In addition to agreeing to the session itself, a therapy agreement includes information about confidentiality and its limitations, cancellation policy, fees, rules around contact in between sessions, and what to do in the event of an emergency or crisis. If you are working with minor clients, your therapy agreement should include information about policies specific to the minor client and their guardian or guardians. There should also be a note referencing your privacy policy and practice information, though in-depth information can be provided in a separate document.

Practice Policies

It is important to provide your client with information about policies you have developed based on your practice needs and to inform them about all laws relevant to your work with them. This includes how you maintain the client's confidentiality and (if you practice in the United States) how you comply with the Health Insurance Portability and Accountability Act (HIPAA). You can also include information about limitations to confidentiality, including mandatory reporting practices, authorizations to release information, and your policy for handling complaints.

Financial Agreement

If your client plans to use health insurance to help pay for the cost of their treatment (more information about this in Chapter 3), you need to gather information about their policy and obtain consent to bill their insurance. Although only limited information is released when you bill, you are acknowledging that you saw the client, the treatment provided, and diagnosis code.

The financial agreement includes authorization to release information to the insurance company and indicates that the client accepts financial responsibility for any costs not covered by insurance. If you are in-network with the insurance company, that contract typically stipulates that you agree to bill the client for co-pays or deductibles, so it is important to have on file.

Additionally, if the client is paying cash for their services, the financial agreement is a contract indicating that they promise to pay the balance due. It is a contract that indicates that they understand what they will be charged. If your practice reserves the right to use collections agencies for unpaid balances, you need a signed financial agreement indicating that the client consents. Otherwise, you do not have consent to release information about their debt to the collections agency.

The financial agreement may indicate information about basic fees but does not indicate the overall cost of services. You might be required to provide more detailed information about the client's estimated cost of care in addition to a financial agreement. This is addressed in Chapter 11.

Social Media

The internet has drastically changed how we live our lives, including therapists. Providers are continuing to navigate having an internet presence (both professional and personal). While it is unreasonable to expect someone to completely opt out of social media, blogs, online reviews, et cetera, based on their job, the online "town square" creates a new set of challenges. We already address how we respond when we meet a client in public, and we must now also address how we manage "running into" a client on social media. Since many platforms allow anonymous engagement, we might not even know that the person responding to our post is a client. Clients might also not realize that messaging on social media platforms is not secure or encrypted.

Additionally, many review websites create profiles for professionals without the professional's consent or knowledge. We must follow specific ethical codes about soliciting testimonials or reviews from current or past clients – depending on the circumstances, this might not be allowed. If a client sees their therapist on Health Grades and thinks the therapist made the profile to solicit reviews, this can unintentionally create an ethical issue for the therapist.

While this can come up with clients of any age, children and teens have a different perspective of what is "professional" or appropriate. As such, it is important to get out in front of these potential issues by having an internet or social media policy to ensure that clients understand how you operate in this space, how you will respond to them, and your boundaries around these websites. As with the other consent paperwork, you should request a guardian signature on this policy, but if your client is active on the internet, you need to make sure they also understand this policy.

Release of Information

This document might not always be necessary, but if it is important to have written consent if you will be communicating with any third parties about your client's treatment. Again, in cases where parents are not married but share custody, you need releases from both of them whenever possible before releasing any information. Additionally, if parents are involved in sessions (for example, for parenting skills work or family therapy), the other parent is not entitled to access those records unless the parent involved in the session consents. This is because, although that parent is not your client, the session still includes their private information.

Samples

On the following pages, you will find sample registration and developmental history forms. Since there is significant variation in how long a developmental history form can be, brief and long developmental history forms are both included so that you can choose what works best in your practice. Additionally, you will find sample wording for consent paperwork, including therapy agreement, financial agreement, privacy policies, and social media policies. Finally, there is a sample release of information form. The wording makes a good starting point for writing up your own paperwork, and you can tailor specifics to how your practice operates or to any nuances in your jurisdiction. The consent forms include spaces for signatures from both parents for ease of use in cases of joint custody, as well as a spot for the client if they are old enough to provide medical consent or if you want your clients to provide assent in writing.

Note: You might choose to combine some of these forms, like making the developmental history part of your registration form or having all office policies listed in the Therapy Agreement. Your goal is to avoid overwhelming the parent or guardian as they put the paperwork together, while ensuring that they thoroughly review the relevant information.

Additional Note: While these samples offer a thorough review of the information needed for the guardian to provide informed consent, it is not enough to simply get a signature. You should also review the consent paperwork at the start of the intake and make sure that the client or guardian fully understands what they agreed to when they signed the paperwork.

Sample Registration Form

Date:________________

Child's full name:________________

Address:________________

Phone number:________________

Email:________________

Consent to calls: Y/N   Consent to texts: Y/N   Consent to voicemails: Y/N

Consent to emails: Y/N

Child's Social Security number: ________________ Child's date of birth:________________

Child's age: ________________ Child's school/grade:________________

Child's gender: ________________ Child's pronouns:________________

Parent 1's name:________________

Parent 1's address (if different from child's):________________

Parent 1's phone number:________________

Parent 1's email:________________

Consent to calls: Y/N   Consent to texts: Y/N   Consent to voicemails: Y/N

Consent to emails: Y/N

Parent 1's gender: ________________ Parent 1's pronouns:________________

Parent 1's employer: ________________ Parent 1's job title:________________

Parent 2's name:________________

Parent 2's address (if different from child's):________________

Parent 2's phone number:________________

Parent 2's email:________________

Consent to calls: Y/N   Consent to texts: Y/N   Consent to voicemails: Y/N

Consent to emails: Y/N

Parent 2's gender: ________________ Parent 2's pronouns:________________

Parent 2's employer: ________________ Parent 2's job title:________________

Who has legal custody?________________

Details about the custody agreement: ________________

Please be aware that I will need a copy of an official custody agreement or court order, if applicable. If parents share custody, I must attempt to reach out to both parents regarding consent to treatment. Depending on your jurisdiction, I may be required to provide access to records and information pertaining to the minor equitably to both parents. Counseling, psychiatric, psychotherapy, and other mental health records are subject to confidentiality and privilege and will only be released in accordance with state and federal law and, if made available to one custodial parent, must be made available to both.

Please initial to indicate understanding of the previous statement:____________________

Who is the child's primary physician?____________________

Clinic:____________________

Address:____________________

Phone number:____________________

Are you willing to sign a release of information for me to communicate with your child's physician regarding their care?____________________

How did you hear about our office?____________________

What previous mental health care has your child received? ____________________

____

____

What is your reason for seeking care now? ____________________

____

____

Is your child currently on any medication? ____________________

____

Sample Developmental History Form (Short)

Date: ______________________

Person completing form: ______________________ Relationship to child: ______________________

Child's name: ______________________

Child's date of birth: ______________________ Child's age: ______________________

Child's address: ______________________

Child's ethnicity: ______________________

Previous addresses: ______________________

____

____

Who has custody? ______________________

Is the child adopted? ______________________

Who currently lives in the home? ______________________

____

____

Describe child's relationship with parents: ______________________

____

____

Describe child's relationship with others in the home: ______________________

____

____

Current school: ______________________ Grade: ______________________

Current concerns related to school: ______________________

____

____

What concerning behaviors are observed in the home? ______________________

____

____

How is discipline handled in the home? ______________________

____

____

Biological family history of mental illness: ____________________

____

____

Significant life events the child has experienced: ____________________

____

____

Traumatic events the child has experienced: ____________________

____

____

Current medical conditions: ____________________

____

____

Past medical conditions: ____________________

____

____

Hospitalizations: ____________________

____

____

Current physician: ____________________

Current medications: ____________________

Describe the child's sleep patterns: ____________________

____

Describe the child's personality: ____________________

____

____

Describe the child's friendships: ____________________

____

____

Does the child have a history of threats or harm to self? ____________________

____

Does the child have a history of threats or harm to others? ____________________

____

Describe any complications with pregnancy or birth: ______________________________
____
____

Describe early developmental delays or concerns: ______________________________
____
____

Describe any early childhood interventions: ______________________________
____
____

Has the child received any previous psychological services? ______________________________
____
____

Has the child ever received academic accommodations? ______________________________
____

Has the child been involved in extracurricular activities? ______________________________
____
____

Has the child used drugs or alcohol? ______________________________
____
____

Has the child gotten into legal trouble? ______________________________
____
____

Additional concerns: ______________________________
____
____
____
____
____
____

Sample Developmental History Form (Long)

Date: ______________________

Person completing form: ______________________ Relationship to child: ______________________

Child's name: ______________________

Child's date of birth: ______________________ Child's age: ______________________

Child's address: ______________________

Child's ethnicity: ______________________

Relevant cultural information: ______________________

____

____

Previous addresses: ______________________

____

____

Who has custody of the child? ______________________

Is the child adopted? ______________________ If yes, at what age? ______________________

What is the child's understanding of the adoption? ______________________

____

____

____

Is there any information about the adoption that the child does not have? ______________________

____

____

____

Who currently lives in the home? ______________________

____

____

Describe the child's relationship with parents: ______________________

____

____

Describe the child's relationship with others in the home: ______________________

____

____

School

Current school: ______________________ Grade: ______________________

Current concerns related to school: ______________________

____

____

Current grades: ______________________

____

____

Current extracurricular activities: ______________________

____

____

Academic history (Complete all that apply):

Grade	*Academics*	*Social Functioning*	*Behavior*	*Other Information*
Kindergarten				
Grade 1				
Grade 2				
Grade 3				
Grade 4				
Grade 5				
Grade 6				
Grade 7				
Grade 8				
Grade 9				
Grade 10				
Grade 11				
Grade 12				

Has the child ever received academic accommodations? ______________________

____

____

Describe the discipline at school: ______________________

____

____

Home

What concerning behaviors are observed in the home? ______________________________

____

____

How is discipline handled in the home? ______________________________

____

____

Biological family history of mental illness: ______________________________

____

____

Significant life events the child has experienced: ______________________________

____

____

Traumatic events the child has experienced: ______________________________

____

____

Describe the child's sleep patterns: ______________________________

____

Describe the child's personality: ______________________________

____

____

Medical

Current medical conditions: ______________________________

____

____

Medical history:

Age	*Diagnoses*	*Medication*	*Interventions*
Infancy (birth–1)			
Ages 1–3			
Ages 4–7			
Ages 8–10			
Ages 11–13			
Ages 13–17			

Current physician: ______________________________

Current medications: ______________________________

Social

Describe the child's friendships: ______________________________

____

____

Does the child choose older, younger, or same-age friends? ______________________________

____

Describe any concerns about social relationships: ______________________________

____

Is the child sexually active? ______________________________

Mental Health

Previous psychological services: ______________________________

____

Previous diagnoses: ______________________________

Biological family mental health history: ______________________________

____

____

Does the child have a history of threats or harm to self? ______________________________

____

Does the child have a history of threats or harm to others? ______________________________

____

Current emotional concerns: ______________________________

____

____

Current behavioral concerns: ______________________________

____

____

Pregnancy

Parental relationship at the time of child's conception: ______________________

____

Was the pregnancy planned? ____________ Were there issues conceiving? ____________

Did either parent consume any substances around the time of conception? ____________

____

____

Did either parent consume any substances during pregnancy? ______________________

____

____

Describe any complications with pregnancy: ______________________

____

____

Describe the birth: ______________________

____

Early Development

Describe any early developmental delays or concerns: ______________________

____

____

Describe any early childhood interventions: ______________________

____

____

Describe the child's temperament in infancy: ______________________

____

Birthing parent's physical health following the birth: ______________________

____

Birthing parent's mental health following the birth: ______________________

____

Non-birthing parent's physical health following the birth: ______________________

____

Non-birthing parent's mental health following the birth: ______________________

____

At what age did the child:

Smile? __________ Roll over? __________ Sit up? __________ Stand up? __________

Crawl? __________ Walk independently? __________ Say first word? __________ Say a full sentence? __________

Describe toilet training: __________

____

Trauma History

Has the child (Please indicate child's age at the time of incident):

Been in a serious accident? __________

Witnessed a serious accident? __________

Been in a natural disaster? __________

Experienced the serious illness of a loved one? __________

Experienced the death of a loved one? __________

Had a serious illness? __________

Undergone a serious medical procedure? __________

Had a serious injury? __________

Been in foster care? __________

Experienced other separation from a parent? __________

Experienced other separation from another family member? __________

Experienced kidnapping? __________

Experienced physical abuse? __________

Experienced the threat of physical abuse? __________

Witnessed physical abuse of someone else? __________

Witnessed the threat of physical abuse to someone else? __________

Experienced community violence? __________

Had a family member imprisoned? __________

Experienced sexual abuse? __________

Attempted sexual abuse? __________

Witnessed sexual abuse? __________

Experienced emotional abuse? __________

Experienced emotional neglect? __________

Experienced physical neglect? __________

Experienced housing instability? __________

Experienced food insecurity? ______________________________

Experienced parental mental illness? ______________________________

Experienced mental illness in another relative? ______________________________

Experienced parental substance dependence? ______________________________

Experienced substance dependence in another relative? ______________________________

Experienced the death of a parent? ______________________________

Experienced bullying? ______________________________

Are there any other events that the child has struggled to handle emotionally? ______________________________

____

____

Occupational History

Has the child worked a job? ______________________________

____

____

Employment history: ______________________________

____

____

Volunteer history: ______________________________

____

____

At-Risk Behavior

Has the child used drugs or alcohol? ______________________________

____

____

Has the child gotten into legal trouble? ______________________________

____

____

Additional concerns: ____

Sample Therapy Agreement With Minors

Confidentiality

The therapeutic relationship is professional, confidential, and protected. All information revealed in this setting is confidential and protected by legal, professional, and ethical standards. All records are confidential and cannot be released without written consent or a signed court order.

In order for therapy to be effective, the client must feel safe and trust the therapist so they can share openly in the therapy environment. If I have reasonable concern that the child is unsafe, I will disclose this information as is legally and ethically required. I may additionally work with the parent/legal guardian to improve communication and support the child outside of sessions. However, the parent/guardian agrees not to request additional information about the child's sessions in order to protect the child's therapeutic relationship. We may discuss specific limitations to this agreement at the start of therapy.

[Include any relevant laws or limitations related to your jurisdiction here.]

Cancellations

If your child is unable to keep their session, it is the guardian's responsibility to let me know that you need to cancel. [Information about your cancellation policy here, including any no-show fees.]

Payment

[Information about when payments are due and what forms of payment you accept.]

Emergencies and Crises

We offer outpatient mental health care that is not appropriate for those who require hospitalization or intensive care. However, crises can emerge for anyone. If your child requires immediate support, please use the following information to receive immediate crisis intervention:

[Include information about local crisis resources here.]

Contact Between Sessions

[Include information about your office hours here, as well as your policies around emails, phone calls, and other contact in between sessions.]

HIPAA Acknowledgement

My privacy policy provides additional information about how I use and disclose Protected Health Information (PHI) as well as how I ensure your confidentiality. The terms are subject to change and, if this occurs, you will receive a revised copy.

By signing this form, you acknowledge that you have received a copy of my privacy policy. If you have questions about this agreement, please ask me.

Client name (print): ______________________________

Today's date: ______________________________

Parent 1 name: ______________________________

Parent 1 signature: ______________________________

Parent 2 name: ______________________________

Parent 2 signature: ______________________________

Client signature: ______________________________

Sample Financial Agreement

Fees

[Include information about the fees for the services you provide here.]

Insurance

If you have medical insurance providing coverage for your psychological service, I will bill your insurance for services rendered. I accept direct reimbursement from your insurance company at your authorization, granted by completing this form. In order to do this, I must have accurate and up-to-date information about your coverage. Please inform me as soon as possible if your plan or coverage changes.

You are encouraged to contact your insurance company prior to making an intake appointment to verify information about coverage, copays, deductibles, or anticipated out-of-pocket costs. You are responsible for any service cost not covered by your insurance plan. Unfortunately, I cannot guarantee what your out-of-pocket cost will be for a service until after I have billed your insurance.

Insurance Information

Insurance company: ______________________________

ID number: ______________________ Group: ______________________

Policy holder: ______________________ Policy holder DOB: ______________________

Client relationship to policy holder: ______________________________

Please initial: ______________ I understand that I am responsible for charges regardless of coverage.

I hereby authorize the release of any information relating to all claims for benefits submitted on behalf of myself and/or my dependents. I further expressly agree and acknowledge that my signature on this document authorizes my provider and [Your Name] to submit claims for benefits without obtaining my signature on each claim to be submitted for my and/or my dependents' care. I will be bound by this signature as though I personally signed each claim.

Client name: ______________________ Date: ______________________

Legal guardian name: ______________________________

Relationship to client: ______________________________

Guardian signature: ______________________________

Sample Privacy Policies

This notice provides information about how your child's psychological and medical information might be used and disclosed and how you can gain access to this information. You can ask questions about this notice. It is subject to change, and you will be provided with a copy if it is updated.

Uses and Disclosures Requiring Authorization

I will use Protected Health Information (PHI) for purposes outside of treatment, payment, and health-care operations if your written authorization is obtained. Written authorization only permits specific disclosures as indicated on the release of information. Outside of legal requirements, I will only release information with your written authorization.

Uses and Disclosures Without Authorization

I am required to disclose PHI without consent or authorization in the following circumstances:

Child abuse: If I have reasonable cause to suspect that a minor has been abused or neglected, I am required by law to report this information to the state Department of Social Services.

Threats to health or safety: If I determine that disclosure of confidential information is necessary to protect you or another person against a clear and substantial risk of imminent harm inflicted by you, I may disclose this information to the person or people who would address this problem (for example, the potential victim or local law enforcement).

Judicial proceedings: If you are involved in a court proceeding and a request is made for information about psychological records, this information is privileged under the law. However, upon receipt of a court order signed by a judge, I must disclose the requested information. I will attempt to contact you in advance of releasing your records, but if I am unable to reach you, I am required to release the records without notifying you. If your child's treatment is court ordered, I may be required to release certain details in compliance with the court order.

Health oversight: If my licensing board is conducting an investigation (for example, if you report me to my licensing board due to a suspected ethical or legal violation), I am required to disclose your records in response to a subpoena from the board in order to cooperate with the investigation.

Questions and Complaints

If you have any questions about this notice or disagree with a decision I made about access to your records, you are encouraged to contact me directly. You are additionally encouraged to contact me about any other concerns about your treatment, privacy, or rights. You can also submit a complaint to [Clinical Director, if applicable] and contact my licensing board:

[Include information about the appropriate licensing board]

Under no circumstances will you be penalized or retaliated against for submitting a complaint.

By signing below, you acknowledge that you have read, agree to, and will abide by the privacy policy.

Client Name (print): ______________________________

Today's Date: ______________________________

Parent 1 Name: ______________________________

Parent 1 Signature: ______________________________

Parent 2 Name: ______________________________

Parent 2 Signature: ______________________________

Client Signature: ______________________________

Sample Social Media Agreement

This document outlines my policies around social media and online engagement. Please read this document to understand my policies around internet engagement and possible interactions that may occur between us online. If you have any questions about this document, please ask. Because technology is continuously changing, this document will be updated as needed. When this occurs, I will provide you with an updated copy.

Connecting and Friending

I do not knowingly accept friend or contact requests from current or former clients on any social networking site, including but not limited to LinkedIn, Facebook, or other similar sites. Doing so can be a violation of your confidentiality if the connection is public, and it blurs the boundaries of the therapeutic relationship.

I will not knowingly send or accept a friend or connection request from you, and I ask that you not send these requests to me. If you use an anonymous account and we connect unintentionally, please inform me so that I can delete the request.

Following

I may have presences on social media websites with posts that are public. I do not ask clients to follow me on social media, but I recognize that I cannot regulate or prevent you from viewing my posts or choosing to follow me. Should you choose to follow my public social media accounts and I recognize your profile, we may briefly discuss this in an appointment in order to explore the potential impact on our therapeutic relationship.

As with connection and friend requests, I will not knowingly follow you back. If your account is anonymous and I do follow you, please let me know so that I can unfollow. This is to preserve the therapeutic relationship and protect your confidentiality. If there are things from your online life that you wish to share with me, you may bring them to an appointment, where we can explore them during your session.

Even if you do not follow me, social media platforms like Facebook and Twitter use algorithms that may show you my content anyway. Please know that, if this is uncomfortable for you, you may block my account to prevent my posts from showing up on your timeline. I will not search for your accounts, and I will not be offended or upset if you set a boundary by blocking me.

Again, I do not request that you read, follow, or comment on any of my public posts. If you choose to seek these posts out, you do so at your own discretion.

Interacting Online

As with in-person encounters that may occur outside of your appointments, I do not seek clients out online. If I recognize that a comment is from a client, I treat it like a comment from someone I do not know in order to preserve your privacy. For example, if I am "liking" several responses to a post, I might also "like" your comment to avoid bringing attention to it as the only comment I did not respond to. These responses will not indicate or acknowledge that you are my client. I will also not engage in ongoing conversation with you on a public platform, even if the comments do not indicate that you are a client.

Please be aware that posts or comments addressing me as your provider or identifying yourself as a client are not confidential, as these are public posts. You make any such posts at your own discretion.

Please never use any social media site's messaging system to contact me. These messages are not encrypted, secure, or HIPAA compliant. I will not reply to you through a social media direct message or private message. If you need to reach me, please use [provide your professional contact information here].

There may be situations where you gain access to my personal, private social media accounts, email, or phone information. Please do not contact me via personal accounts or my private phone number. My professional boundaries include not communicating with clients through my personal accounts or contact information.

If you are in crisis and need immediate support, [include information about your crisis/after-hours support information here].

Email Communications

Email is often the fastest way to get a message to me, and I use an encrypted, HIPAA-compliant system for my professional email communications. Unless your email provider specifically indicates that your emails are secure, you need to be aware that your confidentiality is not protected when you send a new email to me. If you reply to my email, your reply will be secure. All emails sent from my account are secure.

Search Engines

I will not look clients up on search engines except in the most serious of circumstances. For example, if I suspect you are in danger and your emergency contact information is not working, I may search your name in order to find you and check on your personal well-being. If this occurs, I will document the activity and discuss it with you when we next communicate.

You are, of course, welcome to make use of search engines to learn about my credentials, expertise, and business.

Business Review Sites

Dozens of provider business review sites are available online, with automatically generated listings. I have not initiated or created these listings, nor do I monitor them. These sites do not have professional oversight and many include fraudulent reviews.

Additionally, these sites often populate profiles using information they find online, which is often outdated or false. For confidentiality reasons, I do not make profiles on websites that allow or encourage clients to review me. Please be aware that if you see a profile for me on one of these sites, I did not create the profile, the information listed may not be accurate, and I do not monitor the reviews posted on these sites.

If you discover me on one of these sites, please know that my profile does not indicate that I am soliciting a testimonial, rating, or endorsement from you. I will never solicit testimonials from my clients.

Of course, you have the right to express yourself online as you choose. Due to confidentiality, I will not respond to any review on one of these sites, whether it is positive or negative. By posting a review, you compromise your confidentiality as a client. You have the right to post a review if you choose, whether positive, negative, or neutral, but you do so at your own discretion.

If at any time you feel that I have violated my ethics or harmed you in any way, you are welcome to bring this to my attention. You will not be penalized or retaliated against for this. However, if you do not feel comfortable or safe discussing it with me directly, you may also contact [information about supervisor or director, if applicable] or my licensing board at [licensing board information].

By signing below, you acknowledge that you have read, understand, and agree to the social media policy.

Client Name (print): ______________________________

Today's Date: ______________________________

Parent 1 Name: ______________________________

Parent 1 Signature: ______________________________

Parent 2 Name: ______________________________

Parent 2 Signature: ______________________________

Client Signature: ______________________________

Sample Release of Information

Client Name: ______________________ Date: ______________________

Client Date of Birth: ______________________ Client Social Security Number: ______________

I authorize [Business name] and [Therapist name] to release and/or exchange information to

____

Address: ____

Phone Number: ______________________ Fax: ______________________

For the purpose of: ____

I understand that I am authorizing [therapist] to release the information detailed below.

I understand that, unless otherwise indicated, this release is reciprocal, allowing [therapist] and the entity to exchange information.

I understand that I may revoke this release in writing at any time.

I understand that I will be informed of requests for my information.

I understand that I may request to review information being disclosed.

I understand that my information will be transmitted via HIPAA-compliant email, fax, or mail.

I authorize release of the following information (please check all that apply):

__________ Acknowledgement of referral

__________ Past/current assessment

__________ Diagnosis

__________ Case management

__________ Legal orders or filings

__________ Progress notes

__________ Social history

__________ Recommendations

__________ Treatment plans

__________ Medication or medical information

__________ Information about community supports

__________ Discharge summaries

__________ Full medical record

__________ Other (please specify): ______________________________________

This authorization expires: ______________________________

Client Name (print): ______________________________

Today's Date: ______________________________

Parent 1 Name: ______________________________

Parent 1 Signature: ______________________________

Parent 2 Name: ______________________________

Parent 2 Signature: ______________________________

Client Signature: ______________________________

Glossary of Terms

age of majority: The age at which one is considered a legal adult.

assent: An expression of approval or agreement in an official capacity, which can be granted by an individual regardless of age.

authorization: Signing a document giving authority for a specific action.

consent: Official, legal permission to do something or make something happen.

encryption: A method to scramble data so that only authorized parties can access the information.

HIPAA: The Health Insurance Portability and Accountability Act, a 1996 act of Congress in the United States surrounding laws for privacy and confidentiality of health records.

informed consent: Consent to receive a service that includes providing information about the potential risks, limitations, and benefits; specifics of the service provided; and opportunity to ask questions.

Protected Health Information: Identifying information about an individual and the health care they have received.

Works Cited

Age of majority designated as 19 years, AL code § 26–1–1. (2018). https://law.justia.com/codes/alabama/2018/title-26/chapter-1/section-26-1-1/

Examination and treatment of minors, AK code §25–20–025. (2016). https://law.onecle.com/alaska/title-25/25.20.025.html

Health services to minors without parental consent, SC code §65–5–350. (2019). https://law.justia.com/codes/south-carolina/2019/title-63/chapter-5/section-63-5-350/

Marvin and Virginia Schmid law-related education endowment. (2011). *Reaching the age of majority: Your legal rights and responsibilities: A law-related education project of the Nebraska state bar foundation*. www.ned.uscourts.gov/internetDocs/outreach/NSBF-Age-of-Majority-2011.pdf

OECD family database. (2016). *Legal age thresholds regarding the transition from child to adulthood*. Organization for Economic Cooperation and Development. www.oecd.org/els/family/PF_1_8_Age_threshold_Childhood_to_Adulthood.pdf

Senate bill 2355. (2021). http://billstatus.ls.state.ms.us/documents/2021/html/SB/2300-2399/SB2355PS.htm

When a minor may give consent generally, AL code §§22–8–4; 22–8–7. (2013). https://law.justia.com/codes/alabama/2013/title-22/title-1/section-22-8-4

CHAPTER 3

BILLING AND INSURANCE

Many clients either cannot afford the out-of-pocket cost of therapy or simply prefer to use their health insurance to cover the cost of care. You must make sure your billing is accurate and compliant with legal, ethical, and payer standards.

Billing Insurance

If a client or their guardian wants to use insurance to pay for their mental health care, they must authorize the therapist to bill their insurance because the therapist must submit identifying information and certain details about treatment when they bill insurance. This creates limitations to confidentiality while making care more affordable to clients who might not be able to afford the out-of-pocket cost for their sessions.

Insurance companies require information about what service was provided and the diagnosis being treated, and you cannot bill psychological services to insurance companies without a diagnosis. Additionally, some insurance companies and plans do not cover treatment for some diagnoses. This is why it can be helpful to have clients contact their insurance provider prior to scheduling a first session to get information about coverage.

Insurance companies additionally reserve the right to not cover services even if they told a provider or client that a service would be covered. In the previous chapter, the sample financial agreement includes language to ensure that clients understand these policies and that they are out of our hands as providers.

If you accept insurance, you need to know what to include in your progress notes in order to receive reimbursement from insurance companies.

Clinical Documentation and Insurance

Insurance companies vary in requirements. Often, government insurances (Medicare and Medicaid) have specific and strict requirements for providers' treatment plans and progress notes. Always check your local jurisdictional rules to ensure that you are incompliance with any rules or guidelines about your progress notes. The sections detailed previously in this chapter are often required.

When billing insurance, you are required to provide the following information in your claim (a standard claim form is known as a CMS-1500) (CMS Forms):

1. **Client Information:** In order to bill a client's insurance, you must include specific identifying information about the client, including their name, date of birth, plan identification information, and sometimes their social security number. If the client is not the policy holder, information about the policy holder is

DOI: 10.4324/9781003316442-3

also included. Children are often insured through a parent's policy rather than having their own insurance, so it is common for the policy holder to be someone other than the identified client. This ensures that the correct client's plan is billed for the service.

2. **Provider Information:** Providers include their National Provider Identifier (NPI) number, taxonomy code (a code that indicates what their provider qualifications are), and information about the practice, including whether the practice has a separate NPI (sometimes called an NPI Type 2), the practice location or address, payment information for reimbursement, and the Tax Identification Number.
3. **Referral Information:** If applicable, you may need to include a referral from the client's primary physician. Often Medicaid coverage requires this.
4. **Session Information:** This includes the CPT code, date of service, and where the service was performed.
5. **Diagnostic Information:** In order to bill mental health services to insurance, a client must have a diagnosis from the *Diagnostic and Statistical Manual of Mental Disorders* (DSM). The diagnostic information is included in the insurance claim. Be aware that some insurances do not cover certain diagnostic codes, and so if a client has a diagnosis that is not covered, they may not be able to use their insurance to pay for their sessions.

Prior Authorization

Sometimes, insurance companies will require a request of prior authorization before they will approve coverage for a service. This means that the provider must demonstrate that a service is "medically necessary" in order to bill insurance for that service. Depending on the company, you can either call the provider relations phone number or check online to see whether a given service requires prior authorization.

A client might have coverage for a set number of sessions but need prior authorization for additional sessions after that point, or they might need authorization prior to receiving any service. If you need psychological testing in order to develop an appropriate treatment plan, some insurance plans require prior authorization before they will agree to cover the cost of testing.

When submitting a request for prior authorization, you must document why the service is necessary. With children, this often means speaking to how their functioning is impacted in the home, at school, or in other settings. You might have to speak to why the client needs services now rather than waiting until they are older to see whether they "grow out of" the symptoms they are showing.

Health insurance exists to make health care more accessible, but health insurance companies' primary goal is to make profit, not provide the best possible services. Because of this, when requesting prior authorization, it can be effective to speak to how paying for a service now will save them money in the long run. For example, say an insurance company does not want to cover ADHD testing for a six-year-old client because they feel the child is too young to be evaluated. Although ADHD can be diagnosed in children as young as age four, it can be difficult to determine clinically significant hyperactivity compared to developmentally appropriate behavior, and treatment recommendations for ADHD require an accurate diagnosis.

You may indicate that early intervention for ADHD leads to improved mental health and quality of life across the lifespan (Shephard et al., 2022). Basically, paying for an ADHD evaluation now will save them money in the long run when the individual does not require as many other services as they get older.

As providers, of course we would promote early intervention because it is in the client's best interest rather than because it is less expensive. However, we are communicating with insurance companies who do not prioritize well-being over finances, and speaking their language can improve the client's access to care.

Billing Codes

In the United States, therapists who use insurance bill services under Current Procedural Terminology® (CPT) codes to indicate what type of session occurred. CPT codes are trademarked and cover a wide variety of medical procedures, including therapy, and the code used reflects the service provided. There is some ambiguity in CPT codes, and you must use your clinical judgment to determine which code best reflects the session. For example, if a parent or guardian was present for part but not all of the session, you will determine whether the session is most accurately coded as individual therapy or family therapy. Be aware that, if you bill insurance, some policies only cover certain CPT codes, so make sure that the service you render fits with a CPT code covered by the client's plan to ensure payment. The most common CPT codes used in therapy include (billing and coding):

1. **90791:** The diagnostic interview, a 60-minute session in which the therapist gathers extensive background information about the client, is typically the first session, and occurs at the start of therapy. For children, this intake typically includes the guardian's participation in order to gather a thorough history.
2. **90832:** Known as a 30-minute session, this code reflects individual therapy lasting between 16 and 37 minutes.
3. **90834:** The "standard" 45-minute individual therapy session indicates a session lasting 38–52 minutes.
4. **90837:** An individual session lasting 53 minutes or more.
5. **90785:** This code is known as an "Interactive Complexity Add-On" and is used when a therapy session runs over time for a medically necessary reason. For example, if a client states that they feel suicidal just as you are finishing up, you may extend their session to complete a risk assessment, conduct crisis intervention, or make a referral to inpatient care, and you would add this code onto the therapy code. Not all insurance policies allow this add-on.
6. **90847:** This code refers to a family therapy session lasting 26 or more minutes where the client and additional family members are present. Therapists should check the client's insurance coverage before using this code, as it is not always covered. In addition, some insurances allow 90847 to be billed as group therapy, where each family member is a client and their plans are billed separately. However, in order to list each family member as a client, they each must have a diagnosable mental health condition.
7. **90846:** This code is for family therapy sessions where the identified client is not present. For example, if my client is a six-year-old child and I want to explore how the parents can better respond to outbursts and help their child de-escalate, I might need to do this without the child present. I could use this code for parenting sessions used to help the guardian implement therapeutic responses in the home in between sessions or make referrals to additional services that the client might benefit from. Again, this code is not always covered by insurance.
8. **90853:** Group therapy with 2 to 12 participants lasting 45–60 minutes falls under this code. Often, this code is reimbursed at a lower rate than individual therapy, but the therapist makes a progress note and bills a session for every client present for the group.
9. **90849:** Group therapy for multiple families uses this code. Again, group sessions often last 45–60 minutes but may be longer. Some payers do not cover multiple family group therapy.

Audits

Although it is not standard to send the insurance company your full progress notes when you bill for sessions, sometimes insurances will request additional information before processing a claim. For example, they may indicate that they need more evidence that services are "medically necessary" and want additional information prior to paying a claim. They also often conduct audits in which they request session notes for clients on certain dates in order to make sure that the therapist is documenting their work in a way that is compliant with the company's standards and to ensure that providers were not paid inaccurately (Medicare fee for Service Recovery Audit Program).

Because the insurance company could theoretically audit any given session, you must make sure that all of your progress notes follow the insurance company's rules.

Explanation of Benefits

In the previous chapter, we discussed confidentiality and informed consent for minor clients. This includes knowledge of jurisdictional regulations around medical consent. If a client is legally entitled to confidentiality of their medical records, we need that client's consent to provide any information to the parent or legal guardian, including the fact that the individual is a client. For example, if a 17-year-old is entitled to medical confidentiality and is permitted to provide their own consent, that individual must provide consent to communicate with their guardian in any capacity. If that client's parent calls requesting information, we cannot communicate with the parent even though they are a legal guardian outside of specific safety and mandated reporting laws.

If a minor who has confidentiality does not want their legal guardian to know they are receiving services, we have an obligation to follow the law. However, after a service is billed, insurance providers usually send an explanation of benefits to the policy holder indicating what service was billed, what was paid, and an estimate of the client's balance. So if the 17-year-old client from our example does not want their father to know they are meeting with a therapist, but they provide insurance information for which he is the policy holder, he will receive information in the mail that someone on his plan received psychotherapy services. This is also true of young adults who are still on their parents' health insurance.

It is important to communicate to your clients what information will be sent. Typically an Explanation of Benefits is limited to the fact that the client received services, so the guardian does not receive specific details about the sessions.

Samples

Many insurance companies have specific CMS-1500 forms that they want their providers to use, and these forms are often proprietary and subject to copyright. As such, this chapter does not include sample forms for the CMS-1500. Contact your payers regarding what forms they want you to use. Your electronic health record may also have a feature that takes care of this for you.

On the next pages are three sample letters requesting prior authorization from an insurance company. These letters can be customized to be about any specific client when requesting treatment, and they address three common reasons why prior authorization is required for mental health services:

1. You are requesting sessions more frequently than once per week.
2. The payer has indicated that further sessions will not be covered.
3. Your client would benefit from a psychological evaluation.

Sample Preauthorization Letter: Increased Session Frequency

[Date]

[Insurance company contact information]

Re: [Client name and date of birth]

To Whom It May Concern:

I am writing this letter to request preauthorization for therapy sessions for [Client]. I have been seeing [Client] for [brief review of current session frequency and number of sessions]. [Client] has a history of [brief overview of symptoms; include any information about previous crises or hospitalizations]. Based on this, I have diagnosed [Client] with [Diagnosis].

[Client] has been exhibiting [Note increase in symptoms, acuity, severity, et cetera]. It is my professional opinion as [Client's] therapist that they would benefit from [Note about desired frequency of treatment].

Without increased support for their mental health symptoms, [Client] is likely to continue to experience more severe symptoms. Increased session frequency will reduce their need to utilize crisis services and may prevent future hospitalization.

If you have any questions or concerns about this letter, please contact me at [contact information]. I look forward to hearing from you.

Sincerely,

[Your name and credentials]

Sample Preauthorization Letter: Requesting Additional Sessions

[Date]

[Insurance company contact information]

Re: [Client name and date of birth]

To Whom It May Concern:

I am writing this letter to request preauthorization for additional sessions for [Client]. I have been seeing [Client] for [brief review of current session frequency and number of sessions]. [Client] has a history of [brief overview of symptoms; include any information about previous crises or hospitalizations]. Based on this, I have diagnosed [Client] with [Diagnosis].

[Include a brief overview of your treatment so far; preserve your client's confidentiality by speaking to specific symptoms, such as depressed mood, panic attacks, et cetera rather than specific identifying information. Example follows.]

Through therapy so far, [Client] has exhibited decreased panic symptoms, with attacks occurring approximately once per week rather than three times per week. However, [Client] continues to struggle with leaving the house due to acute anxiety, and weekly panic attacks continue to interfere with their ability to function. [Client] requires ongoing care to continue the progress they have made and to prevent symptoms from increasing should they lose access to treatment.

[Note: If your client's diagnosis is chronic, you can indicate that the number of sessions previously approved did not fully alleviate symptoms because that is not a realistic treatment expectation. Speak to how ongoing therapy services can prevent symptoms from getting worse or improve functioning and quality of life. Example follows.]

Since [Diagnosis] is a lifelong condition, it is likely that [Client] will need ongoing access to therapy treatment and support. [Client] has shown significant improvement in [specific examples of improvement] since starting therapy services. Ongoing access to care will prevent relapse in symptoms.

If you have any questions or concerns about this letter, please contact me at [contact information]. I look forward to hearing from you.

Sincerely,

[Your name and credentials]

Sample Preauthorization Letter: Psychological Evaluation

[Date]

[Insurance company contact information]

Re: [Client name and date of birth]

To Whom It May Concern:

I am writing this letter to request preauthorization for a psychological evaluation for [Client]. [Client] is referred by [referral source] for a psychological evaluation because they have a history of [brief overview of symptoms and history].

Following an intake interview on [Date], I have provisionally diagnosed [Client] with [Diagnosis], as well as a rule-out for [Condition for evaluation]. This is based on [note of client's report of existing symptoms].

Psychological testing is needed to confirm or rule out [Client's] provisional diagnosis and rule-out. These diagnoses have different best practices for evidence-based treatment, and an accurate diagnosis is needed to prevent [Client's] mental health from worsening, which may then require more intensive interventions to treat.

An accurate diagnosis can offer beneficial treatment recommendations and appropriate interventions that will improve [Client's] quality of life, alleviate their symptoms, and prevent the need for more intensive care in the future. The requested evaluation will provide this clarification.

In order to conduct the evaluation, I am requesting [specific CPT codes and quantities].

[If requited by the payer, you may also need to list the specific testing measures you will be using. Check with the payer before submitting your preauthorization request to determine whether this information is needed.]

If you have any questions or concerns about this letter, please contact me at [contact information]. I look forward to hearing from you.

Sincerely,

[Your name and credentials]

Glossary of Terms

audit: In therapy, this refers to when a payer requests to inspect the details of a clinician's notes in order to ensure compliance.

CMS-1500: The form used to bill therapy sessions to insurance.

CPT Code®: Current Procedural Terminology Codes used by providers to indicate the specific service or services provided in an appointment.

electronic health record: Digital medical charts that are encrypted and HIPAA-compliant.

family therapy: Therapy services that involve multiple members of a client's family.

group therapy: Therapy involving one or more clients meeting together who may share a diagnosis, history, or demographic.

individual therapy: Psychotherapy in which an individual meets with a therapist one-on-one to treat their mental health symptoms.

health insurance: A contract with an insurer to pay some or all health care costs in exchange for the client's premium payments.

medically necessary: A term indicating that a client has a documented medical need for a service.

NPI: National Provider Identifier, an identification number assigned to a provider linking them to their specialty and scope of practice.

NPI Type 1: An NPI for an individual provider.

NPI Type 2: An NPI for an organization.

policy holder: The person named in an insurance policy. The policy holder may have a policy that covers a spouse or dependents.

Tax Identification Number: A tax processing number for a business.

Taxonomy Code: A 10-digit code that indicates the provider's specialization and scope of practice.

Works Cited

Billing and coding: Psychiatry and psychology services. (n.d.). *CMS.gov centers for Medicare & Medicaid services*. Retrieved December 24, 2022, from www.cms.gov/medicare-coverage-database/view/article.aspx?articleId=57480

CMS forms. (n.d.). *CMS*. Retrieved December 24, 2022, from www.cms.gov/Medicare/CMS-Forms/CMS-Forms

CPT® (current procedural terminology). (n.d.). *Current procedural terminology*. American Medical Association. Retrieved December 24, 2022, from www.ama-assn.org/amaone/cpt-current-procedural-terminology

Medicare fee for service recovery audit program. (n.d.). *CMS*. Retrieved December 24, 2022, from www.cms.gov/research-statistics-data-and-systems/monitoring-programs/medicare-ffs-compliance-programs/recovery-audit-program

Shephard, E., Zuccolo, P. F., Idrees, I., Godoy, P. B. G., Salomone, E., Ferrante, C., Sorgato, P., Catão, L. F. C. C., Goodwin, A., Bolton, P. F., Tye, C., Groom, M. J., & Polanczyk, G. V. (2022). Systematic review and meta-analysis: The science of early-life precursors and interventions for attention-deficit/hyperactivity disorder. *Journal of the American Academy of Child & Adolescent Psychiatry, 61*(2), 187–226. https://doi.org/10.1016/j.jaac.2021.03.016

CHAPTER 4

INTAKES AND DIAGNOSTIC INTERVIEWS

You're about to go into an intake for a new client. The client is a child who is too young to provide their own history. What information do you need to gather in this appointment? What questions do you need to ask? What goes into a thorough developmental history? What happens when the client and parent disagree?

What Is an Intake?

Usually, therapy or other psychological services start with an intake or diagnostic interview. During an intake appointment, the provider gathers detailed history about the client, including current symptoms, history of symptoms, family history, development, and many other areas. When an adult comes for an intake session, they often attend the appointment alone and are the only source of this knowledge, unless they choose to bring a second person either for support or to provide additional history. Even if this is the case, typically the identified client is the primary source of information during the intake.

With children and teens, though, you often meet with a parent or guardian as well as your client. This means you can get information about early development that most people might not remember about themselves, as well as an outside perspective on the client's symptoms. It also means, though, that you may have to note opposing reports about symptoms.

Who Attends an Intake?

Depending on your practice (and payer requirements), you may have the option to see the parent or guardian individually before meeting your client. If this is an option, it can be beneficial to talk with the guardian alone for several reasons:

1. There may be aspects of the client's history that the guardian has not disclosed to them, and they might withhold this information from you if the client is present; for example, if the client does not know they are adopted. (Your professional opinion may be that the child should have this information, and the parent should tell them as soon as possible. However, your office during an intake appointment is neither the time nor the place for this kind of revelation.)
2. The client may have a history of trauma that has not yet been addressed, and the guardian disclosing this trauma in front of the client could be triggering. If the client is present for the session, the guardian must choose between giving you the full history and avoiding this trigger. If they disclose and the client becomes escalated, you might not be able to finish getting the history because you have to address the client's emotional response to the information.

DOI: 10.4324/9781003316442-4

3. The child may have behavioral issues that are very frustrating for the guardian. The guardian might need to describe these behaviors to you as part of the history, and overhearing this discussion might give the child the impression that they are meeting with you because they have done something wrong and are in trouble. You can address the guardian's feelings and even validate their frustration without having to worry about the impact of the discussion on the client.
4. The guardian might have questions for you that are not appropriate to ask in front of the child. For example, the guardian might worry that the child's symptoms mean they will never be able to live independently, and hearing this might be harmful to the child. If the guardian wonders these things, it is important for them to be able to ask a professional their questions in a safe environment.
5. You might want to give the guardian feedback on parenting choices. While parenting skills training can be an important part of therapy with minors, giving this feedback in front of the client can undermine the guardian's role as an authority figure.
6. The guardian and the client may have different perspectives on the "problem" that led to them seeking therapy. Meeting with the guardian individually grants you the opportunity to build rapport with the guardian without risking alienating the client. Additionally, it can be helpful to have detailed information about these differences of opinion, and meeting with the guardian without the client present can allow you to ask questions and gather this information without causing an argument between the client and their caregiver.

On the other hand, you might decide that the client should be present for the intake. Reasons for making this decision may include:

1. If the client has a history of mistrust about medical systems or trauma related to past care, meeting with the guardian individually might make it more difficult for the client to trust you from the start. It is generally not a good idea to lie to clients, so if you meet with the guardian first, most of the time the client will be aware of this at some point.
2. Based on the family's culture or personal values, the guardian may feel it is more appropriate for the client to be present for the intake session.
3. If the client is at the age of medical consent in your jurisdiction, even if they are still a minor, they might have the legal right to be present during the intake interview. (Read more about age of medical consent in Chapter 2.)

It can be helpful to share these potential issues with the guardian when they schedule the intake. They might have an opinion on whether or not it is appropriate for the child to be present for the intake or to be present only for part of the intake.

When Parents Aren't Together

When working with minors, we often run into situations where our client has more than one legal guardian and those legal guardians are not in a relationship with each other. Always document who has legal guardianship or custody of your client and note how you confirmed this information. For example, if a child has parents who are divorced, request a copy of the most current custody order. Although we cannot guarantee that a guardian will never lie to us about custody, we can note that we did our best to ensure that we followed laws and ethics surrounding that client's care. (More detailed information about documenting legal guardianship is available in Chapter 2 of this book.)

Sometimes, only one parent will attend an intake session. This can be sufficient in gathering the client's background information and is common when the parents are married. However, if a child has more than one household, it can be beneficial for the therapist to gather information about how symptoms may vary across households, as well as rules and expectations in each home. You must determine the most appropriate way to gather this information, which will depend on the individual family.

Again, the goal of that intake is to gather a thorough history. Will having both parents present lead to an argument that derails the session and prevents you from getting the information that you need? It might be helpful to meet with each parent separately if there is a lot of conflict in the relationship. However, if the parents are on amicable terms, they might be able to meet with the provider together without issue.

Consider also your skill set and therapeutic approach. If you are a trained mediator with experience navigating difficult conversations between high-conflict couples, you might feel more prepared to deal with potential arguments in an intake session compared to someone who has not done this kind of work.

Parents may have different perspectives on how civil or amicable their relationship is, and they might tell you that they get along well in most situations but find themselves butting heads when discussing their child's mental health in your office. You can make it your policy that intakes are done separately if this works best for you, as long as you make sure to outline this and communicate it clearly. You might also decide to determine what is most appropriate on a case-by-case basis and ask parents what feels most comfortable for them.

When presenting these options to parents, normalize that some conflict is to be expected. After all, if they got along perfectly, they would probably be together. If one parent states that they feel uncomfortable or unsafe with a joint intake, it is often best to honor that request and do separate appointments. Just like a parent might not be fully forthcoming about their child's symptoms in front of the child, a parent who feels uncomfortable expressing themselves in front of the other parent might leave out details that are important for the therapist to know.

Regardless of your decision, document what the best choice was for each situation and how you came to that conclusion.

Parts of the Intake

A thorough intake includes many components. This can feel overwhelming, but remember that much of this information might come up naturally as you go over various sections of the intake. It can help to take notes throughout the appointment and take time later to organize the information.

- **Client's identifying information:** The client's name, date of birth, et cetera
- **Payment information:** Insurance, self-pay, billing code, et cetera
- **Date, time, and length of session:** When you met and for how long
- **Location of the session:** If you see clients in person, this will usually be your office. However, for telehealth sessions, you will also need to note where participants physically were at the time of the session. This can simply indicate that they were at home if you have that address on file.
  - **Telehealth safety/privacy:** If the client is seen via telehealth, you need to also document that you confirmed that the client was in a location where it was physically safe to join the session and that they had privacy during the session. This is often as simple as, "Therapist asked the client if they were alone, and the client stated that no one else was present. Therapist did not note any indication that anyone else was present in the session."
  - **Telehealth security:** Note what platform was used for telehealth sessions as well as an indication confirming that the platform was secure and utilized technology compliant with your jurisdictional requirements for protecting confidentiality and privacy.

  - **Telehealth justification:** You may also note why a session was conducted via telehealth. For example, in April 2020, every note I wrote stated that the session was conducted via video due to safety concerns related to the COVID-19 pandemic. You might indicate that the client was seen via telehealth due to their physical distance from your office, health concerns, transportation issues, or the client's personal preference. Always check with your licensing board and any payers regarding whether there are limitations to providing telehealth, such as insurance companies refusing to cover telehealth if the client is within a certain distance of your office. These requirements have become more flexible in recent years. (What to include in this justification will be explored in more detail in Chapter 8.)

- **Who was present:** Was the client present for all or part of the session? Which guardian or guardians were present? If the client is in foster care or state custody, was a foster parent or social worker present? Note also why anyone present was there. If the client was not present, note your justification for this choice.

- **Presenting concern:** Why was this appointment made? What is the issue that led to scheduling this intake? Be succinct and precise in this area. More details will be provided later.

- **Safety assessment:** Risk assessments are covered in more depth in Chapter 10 of this text. However, it is important to note that providers must assess for safety during an intake, including asking about history of safety concerns that may no longer be relevant.

- **Mental status examination:** Mental status examinations (MSE) are covered in Chapter 7 of this text. If the client is present for the intake, there should be a note about MSE in the intake note with details about how they presented for this appointment.

- **Informed consent:** Specifics of informed consent paperwork are discussed in Chapter 2. It is important to cover informed consent prior to starting treatment. The guardian should have signed paperwork detailing this information, but providers must ensure that they have made space to address any questions related to this. Additionally, if the parent or guardian signed off on the informed consent, this does not mean that a minor client is aware and has also provided assent to treatment. Review this policy, including confidentiality limitations, and document that this occurred as part of the intake.

- **Diagnostic interview:** In this section, you will detail all the information shared with you by your client and/or their guardian(s) or representative(s). Make sure to document the source of each piece of information. For example, if the parent indicates that they have observed anxiety in the client, note that the information came from the parent. A thorough diagnostic interview includes several categories. The categories presented here can be documented in any order that best fits your clinical style and preference:

  - **Identifying information:** Include the client's legal name, preferred name, gender, pronouns, age, location of current residence, where they are from, and who lives in the home.

  - **Cultural information:** Describe the client's nationality, the parents' nationalities, any culturally significant information about the family, any information about religious affiliation, and the client's and parents' racial or ethnic backgrounds.

  - **Demographic history:** This is a quick timeline of where the client has lived and with whom as caretaker. As much as possible, include specific dates or ages of moves and changes.

  - **Presenting symptoms:** What mental health symptoms is the client currently dealing with? How long have these symptoms been present? What do they look like specifically? How do they impact the client's functioning?

  - **History of symptoms:** What symptoms has the client experienced in the past that might not be present now?

  - **Treatment history:** What, if any, treatment has the client had in the past related to their mental health? Past evaluations? Hospitalizations related to their psychiatric symptoms? Medications? Note also what the client found helpful or unhelpful (if they are comfortable sharing this information), any history of medication side effects, et cetera.

- **Family history:** You can create a genogram for this information if you find it helpful. (An example is available at the end of this chapter.) You can also present this information in a narrative format. Include who the client's relatives are and note biological connections (full biological sibling, half biological sibling [note on which side], adoptive sibling, foster sibling). Also note who is active in the client's life – are there biological family members who are estranged? Who, and why? What is the client's understanding of these relationships? Does the guardian disclose anything about the client's knowledge of their family that the client is not aware of? A thorough family history gives you the context for your client's life and upbringing, and it can shed light on intergenerational patterns and the possibility for epigenetic trauma (Berger et al., 2009). Include information about any family history of diagnosed or suspected mental health issues and symptoms.
- **Developmental history:** A thorough developmental history starts well before the child was born. Gather information about what was going on for the parents around the time of conception, whether either parent used substances around that time or through the pregnancy, and the quality of their relationship. Note whether there were fertility concerns and whether any treatments were used to aid in implantation. Ask about stressors during the pregnancy and any medical issues the parent had while pregnant. Ask also about the birth, whether it was full-term, induced, caesarian section, or vaginal, and gather information about the client's health when they were born. Did they have to stay in the NICU? For how long? Were they able to spend time with the parent or parents immediately after birth? Ask also about milestones, including rolling over, standing, walking, first words, sentences, toilet training, motor skills, and socialization. It can help to have a developmental history template to ensure that you do not miss any vital information.
- **Adaptive functioning:** Does the client seem to be functioning at a level that is developmentally appropriate? What kinds of things do they still need help with, and what things do they do independently? For teen clients, have they started driving, and if not, is there a reason? This section includes extensive information about what the client's day-to-day life looks like based on their support needs.
- **Trauma history:** Sometimes you can get more accurate information about a client's trauma history by minding the language that you use. Both guardians and clients might not consider certain events to be "traumatic" but will endorse things that are objectively stressful and difficult to manage. It can help to use a specific screening inventory that asks about a variety of specific events, or you can ask an open-ended question about a history of stressors. Many free trauma inventories are available online.
- **Current medical issues:** List any current medical diagnoses the client has, including any medications they are taking at this time, both prescribed and over-the-counter. How long have they been on the medications, and do the medications have any side effects that they are aware of?
- **Medical history:** Describe any past hospitalizations, surgeries, or health concerns. Note here also previous medications the client has taken and when they discontinued taking them.
- **Educational history:** What grade is the child in? Have they repeated a grade? How many different schools have they attended? Get information about subjects they struggle with or excel in, any accommodations, IEPs, or 504 plans. Note any behavioral concerns at school as well as both positive and negative feedback from teachers. Note also whether the client is involved in extracurricular activities, how often, and their feelings about these activities.
- **Employment history:** With young children, this section is likely irrelevant. However, you may want to note whether a middle school-aged client has done anything to earn money outside the home, like babysitting or helping the neighbors with lawn care. Teen clients might have worked various jobs.
- **Social history:** What are the client's social supports? How do they do with making friends? What kind of friends do they tend to choose? Do they experience a lot of conflict in their friendships? If the client has dated, also note information about any history of dating or romantic relationships, including whether the client is sexually active.

  - **Substance use history:** Has the client experimented with alcohol, tobacco, marijuana, or other drugs? When, and how many times? Are there any substances they use regularly? Do they drink caffeine, and if so, how much and in what quantity?
  - **Legal history:** Has the client gotten into trouble with law enforcement? What was happening? How did the parents respond? Note any pending charges, probation, et cetera.
  - **Client interests:** Especially if you will be seeing this client for ongoing therapy services, it is important to gather information about what the client likes or does not like. You can use their areas of interest to build rapport and to show that you care about them as a person beyond their presenting symptoms.
  - **Client strengths:** Many people come to an intake session because they (or their child) are having a hard time. The client might feel down on themselves because of the difficulties they are experiencing. If the client is presenting with behavioral issues, the parent might also feel frustrated and have difficulty seeing the positives about their child. Assessing the client's strengths reminds them that there are things the client is good at, things the client does well, and things the client can be praised for. This also helps you incorporate the client's strengths into their treatment plan.
  - **Other information:** A diagnostic interview contains a huge amount of information about one person. Humans are complex, so no matter how thorough you are, there is always the possibility that the client will feel that there is relevant information that was not included. Make space at the end of the intake to let the client share any additional information that might not have been addressed elsewhere.
- **Next steps/plan:** You do not necessarily have to have a fully fleshed-out treatment plan by the end of an intake interview, but note any relevant details about what the client and their parent(s) or guardian(s) hope to get out of seeking your services. Chapter 6 of this text details the development of a thorough treatment plan. During the intake, though, you do need to know what your next steps are. If the diagnostic interview only included the guardian, when will you meet with the client? If you need more assessment information, what assessments will you use, and how will these be distributed? Does the parent or guardian need to send you additional records to review? This section details the plan of action following the intake.
- **Diagnosis:** Chapter 5 details developing a diagnostic impression with child and teen clients. Depending on your jurisdiction, organizational policies, and payer requirements, determine whether you need to include any diagnostic information at the time of the intake. If needed, you can grant a "provisional" diagnosis, meaning that you are acknowledging the limitations of the information you presently have available to you, and you will update the diagnosis as you gather more information. You can also note whether you are going by another provider's diagnosis. For example, if a child was diagnosed with ADHD during a school assessment, you might input the ADHD diagnosis "per history" for your intake if you have sufficient information. You might also note an anxiety or mood disorder that a previous therapist diagnosed.

"Information Not Provided"

A thorough diagnostic interview covers a lot of ground, but many intake sessions are only 60 minutes in length. Sometimes providers can set aside 90 minutes for an intake, but this still might not be a sufficient amount of time, especially if the child has a complicated history. Although children's total life experience is shorter than adults, various events have more significance due to the client's young age. Consider using tools such as timelines to document when things such as stressful or traumatic events, moves, or changes in caregiver took place.

There may be situations where your diagnostic interview does not have to include every piece listed here. For example, if the intake is a component of an evaluation for a specific diagnosis, you might focus on those symptoms rather than the full history.

There will likely be situations where all of the information is not available. Children who have been in the foster system might not have full history information. Note what information was not available and, if applicable, why that information was not included.

Sources of Information

As you document information during an intake interview, note where each piece of information came from. Is this something the client told you directly, or did the information come from the guardian? What information came from reviewing other records?

If the guardian, caseworker, school, or other source provided you with records, note what was shared in the intake appointment itself and document those records separately to clarify what was and was not part of the intake interview. Note also that records generated by another professional and provided to you to assist with your work with the client are not part of your chart. If, for example, a lawyer requests a client's "full chart," this only includes records that you generated for the client. The sample release of information in Chapter 2 notes that the release does not authorize the recipient of those records to pass them on further. A request for this information must go to the provider who generated the records or their representative.

Often, when we get information about a client from more than one source, we will encounter conflicting stories. In this case, carefully note each person's perspective and the disparity. For example, "Parent stated that client has periods of two to three days when they do not get out of bed. Client, however, stated that they get out of bed every day but sometimes return to bed after a few hours."

In most contexts, it is not the mental health provider's role to figure out whether someone is being dishonest. We are not police, detectives, or investigators. We merely note the information told to us and whether there is a contradiction or contraindication.

Language Note

Whenever possible, use your client's own words or the words of the source of your information. We are often tempted to put clinical language into our notes, which can be appropriate, but note what the client or their representative said specifically when demonstrating how that clinical conclusion applies.

Confidentiality Agreements

It is important to be upfront, transparent, and specific with legal guardians regarding how you handle confidentiality around minor clients' therapy records. Guardians should not be taken by surprise if you inform them that you will not release specific session information. This should be noted in your consent paperwork (Chapter 2) and discussed during the intake.

If the client is not present for the intake, let the guardian know your policies around confidentiality and its limitations. Ask them what their expectations are regarding confidentiality in their child's therapy sessions. If the client is present, have a discussion about what confidentiality means and what everyone expects around privacy.

You may feel that it is appropriate to have set policies around minor clients' confidentiality in their therapy sessions, to put those policies in your intake paperwork, and to enforce the same expectation with all clients. On the other hand, you may feel that a case-by-case approach is a better fit for your practice. Some guardians will feel very uncomfortable knowing that a confidentiality policy is inflexible and may choose to take their child to another provider if you are unwilling or unable to work with them or compromise. On the other hand, a child might not feel comfortable sharing anything with a provider who might disclose to their parents.

If you choose to have flexibility with your confidentiality policy, it is even more important to have everyone's expectations addressed and to be on the same page at the start of treatment. In this case, you might draw up a confidentiality agreement with the family and have the guardian(s) and client all sign, indicating that they understand what they are agreeing to and the limitations to confidentiality in this setting.

Samples

This chapter includes two sample intake templates, with a blank template of each provided for easy reproduction. First is an open-ended template that allows you to structure the client's narrative in whatever way seems to best fit them as an individual. The second is more organized and can make it easier to find a specific piece of information.

This section also includes a sample questionnaire that includes questions about thorough developmental history and trauma screening. You can use the sample questionnaire to guide your intake interview or tweak it to fit your needs.

This chapter additionally includes sample information for constructing a genogram. A genogram can be helpful in organizing and displaying extensive family information in a way that makes it easy to find and assess. However, genograms present some limitations, as they historically focus on a "nuclear family" and typically reinforce binary views around gender (Barsky, 2022). If a visual map of the client's family is helpful, a genogram is a good starting point for displaying this information, but remember to be flexible to ensure that you accurately and adequately display information specific to your client and their needs. This might mean developing new symbols and exploring existing options for expanded genogram symbols (Keith, 2013).

Finally, a sample confidentiality agreement is included, since this is something that will be established at intake if the client is present or shortly afterward if the parent attends the intake alone. Please be aware that the sample included is a hypothetical example. For instance, it notes that the fictional guardians want information about the client's substance use, which you may not deem necessary to share. It is not an indication of best practice surrounding limitations to confidentiality. Use your professional judgment in drawing up these agreements in your practice.

Note: Usually an intake or diagnostic interview would include additional information, such as a mental status examination and a diagnosis. These components are addressed later in the book (diagnoses in Chapter 4 and mental status examinations in Chapter 7) and are thus not included in these templates.

Sample Intake Interview: Open Narrative

This example does not include a blank form, as an open narrative is just a blank page.

Social history information is provided by J and his legal guardians, and the following information is presented per their report. J is a 15-year-old boy in the custody of his paternal aunt and uncle, and he lives with them and his two younger brothers (ages 12 and 6). J was born in (location) and presently lives in (location). He has no contact with his biological parents at this time. The parents are permitted visitation but have not exercised this opportunity for approximately one year. The guardians reported that J would exhibit increased behavioral outbursts for about three days following visits.

J was born about four weeks prematurely and was given a heart monitor after he was born. His overall health was good, and the heart monitor was a precautionary measure. He experienced developmental delays in crawling, walking, and talking, though this may have been due in part to neglect. His biological parents reportedly kept him in a car seat most of the time and did not permit him to interact with other children or play outside.

J first moved in with his guardians when he was one year old because his parents were evicted from their residence and unable to provide housing for him. The move was intended to be temporary, but due to housing instability, he remained in their care until age three. During a visit with his current guardians at age four, J disclosed physical abuse by both biological parents and that he had witnessed domestic violence between the parents. The guardians reported this to Child Protective Services and filed for guardianship at this time.

J has seen several therapists throughout his life. His guardians had him start play therapy when they first got custody, and J has participated in both individual and group therapy for trauma, social skills, and behavioral issues. J was hospitalized for one week in [Date] for suicidal ideation, and he was re-admitted six months later for self-harm behavior, including cutting and hitting his head.

J has difficulty making and keeping friends. He tends to be "bossy" in social relationships and prefers to interact with younger children. He plays on the football and baseball teams, and he wants to try out for the basketball team this year.

At this time, J is in the ninth grade. He repeated kindergarten due to lack of academic support as well as learning delays, and he has a history of difficulty with reading. His schooling has been disrupted by hospitalizations. He has difficulty sustaining attention in the classroom, and he has difficulty managing frustration if he does not understand his schoolwork. He currently has an IEP that allows him to take breaks to regulate and gives him extra support with reading and English.

J has reported intrusive memories of abuse from his biological parents, including feeling like he is re-living these experiences. He stated that this occurs daily, and he feels constantly "on edge" and fearful that the memories will surface or that he will be in danger again. He often copes by becoming engrossed in fantasies and daydreams where "everything is good."

Medically, J has a history of asthma but does not presently require intervention for this. He was exposed to secondhand cigarette smoke when living with his mother but has not smoked or used any drugs per his report. He has no known medical issues. At this time, he takes [Medications] for his mental health symptoms.

Sample Intake Interview: Categories

Identifying information: F is a 16-year-old girl living in [Location] in a group home setting. She was referred to the group home six months ago due to repeatedly running away from her maternal grandmother, who is her legal guardian. She is originally from [Location]. She has not lived in any other geographic areas. She is cisgender and heterosexual. Both parents have had rights terminated, and she does not presently have contact with them.

Presenting concern: F is referred for an evaluation that is required by the state in order to secure funding for her group home placement. She has a previous diagnosis of an intellectual disability as well as significant trauma history. This assessment aims to provide current information about her cognitive and functional abilities as well as recommendations regarding her placement. She was referred to the group home due to repeatedly running away from her grandmother's house, which she states she did because she dislikes her grandmother's rules and expectations.

Safety assessment: F has been hospitalized twice for suicidal ideation, with the first hospitalization occurring at age 14. She was hospitalized approximately one month prior to this intake. She denied a history of suicide attempts and endorsed ongoing passive thoughts, which she processes with her regular therapist. Group home staff are aware of her history and current thoughts, and a safety plan is in place.

Cultural information: F reports that her father is Native American and a member of [Tribal affiliation], and her mother is Black. She described herself as agnostic and not practicing a religion.

Demographic history: F was born in [Town] and lived there until moving to [Town] at age three, when her grandmother took over her care.

Presenting symptoms: F's caseworker reports that F tends to be irritable with staff, though this has improved somewhat. She presently has outbursts approximately once per week during which she screams and swears, though no physical aggression was reported. F verified this and stated that she is working on improving this behavior. She reported that she experiences nightmares about three times per week and is anxious "most of the time."

History of symptoms: F has a history of depressive episodes, and she reported first experiencing these symptoms at approximately age ten. She reports periods of two weeks to one month where she feels down, does not want to get out of bed, and struggles to enjoy things. Regarding the nightmares, F states that she has had them "all my life" and that they often include memories from early childhood. She also reports being "jumpy" and feeling like something bad might happen at any moment.

Treatment history: F received treatment during two psychiatric hospitalizations noted earlier. She has had several individual, outpatient therapists, and she currently sees a therapist weekly who comes to the group home. She first started therapy at age five, when her grandmother brought her for treatment due to "tantrum" behaviors that were concerning. F states that she likes her current therapist and feels she can share in her sessions.

Family history: F has an older half-brother on her mother's side and two older half-sisters on her father's side. There is family history of substance dependence, ADHD, bipolar disorder, depression, and anxiety.

Developmental history: F was born at approximately 28 weeks' gestation following a pregnancy complicated by gestational diabetes. The pregnancy was high-risk, and the mother's water broke two days before the birth. F contracted asthma and pneumonia as a newborn and spent several weeks in the NICU due to premature birth and illness. She weighed four pounds and eight ounces at birth. She experienced developmental delays in walking and language, but other milestones were reportedly reached within normal limits. There may have been alcohol use during the pregnancy, but this has not been confirmed.

Adaptive functioning: F attempts to help with cooking at the group home when asked but requires supervision when using the stove or oven. She takes medication when provided by staff, and due to group home rules, she is not allowed to do this independently. F is usually able to engage in daily self-care activities like hygiene and dressing herself, though staff have noted that she resists getting out of bed at times. F said that this occurs when she is experiencing a depressive episode.

Trauma history: F lived with her biological parents from birth to age three, and during this time she reportedly experienced physical neglect, parental drug use in the home, and she may have been present for physical altercations between her parents, though F states that she does not remember this. Child Protective Services became involved because a neighbor called 911 due to the father assaulting the mother, and F was taken into care. She was placed with her maternal grandmother and has lived with her since age 3. No history of neglect or abuse was reported while in her grandmother's care.

Current medical issues: F takes 50 mg Zoloft daily for her depression and anxiety, and she has been on this dose for one year. She stated she does not know whether it is helpful. She has an inhaler for asthma. No history of head trauma is reported, and no other current medical issues were reported.

Medical history: F did not have regular medical care prior to age three due to neglect. When she was taken into care, she was underweight and had medical issues related to malnutrition. She was treated for this with outpatient care. No history of surgeries was reported.

Educational history: F is a tenth-grade student. She attended [School] before her group home placement and presently attends online school through the group home. She has an IEP for her intellectual disability and receives accommodations for reading and math. Her grades are primarily Bs and Cs, and she is not currently failing any classes.

Employment history: F has not been employed.

Social history: F has one close friend she has known since childhood, but she has not had contact with this friend since transitioning to the group home. She does not seek companionship from peers in the group home and stated that there is "no point," as she hopes to return to her grandmother's care. She reportedly has had few friends throughout her life and does not initiate friendships or socializing with classmates. F stated that she does not have a history of dating or romantic relationships.

Substance use history: F is not presently drinking or using drugs due to group home policy. She reportedly has experimented with vaping nicotine but denied habitual use. She stated that she tried alcohol on one occasion when she found a bottle of vodka at her grandmother's house but did not like the taste.

Legal history: Law enforcement became involved due to F running away from home on three occasions (approximately two years ago, one year ago, and six months ago). The grandmother called law enforcement on all three occasions due to not being able to locate F. She was not formally charged but was referred to this level of care on the third occasion to prevent future absconding.

Interests and strengths: F is a musician and plays guitar. She enjoys watching other guitar players on YouTube to learn new techniques.

Other information: Maternal grandmother is the legal guardian and provided consent. F describes this relationship as good overall but noted that she gets "really mad" when the grandmother sets boundaries she does not like.

Next steps/plan: In order to comply with state requirements for her placement, F will complete an IQ and functional assessment. Additional testing for emotional issues will also be completed for treatment planning purposes. She will continue therapy sessions with her primary therapist.

Sample Intake Interview: Categories (Blank)

Identifying information: __________

Presenting concern: __________

Safety assessment: __________

Cultural information: __________

Demographic history: __________

Presenting symptoms: __________

History of symptoms: __________

Treatment history: __________

Family history: ______________________________

____

____

____

Developmental history: ______________________________

____

____

____

Adaptive functioning: ______________________________

____

____

____

Trauma history: ______________________________

____

____

____

Current medical issues: ______________________________

____

____

____

Medical history: ______________________________

____

____

____

Educational history: ______________________________

____

____

____

Employment history: ______________________________

____

____

____

Social history: ______________________________

Substance use history: ______________________________

Legal history: ______________________________

Interests and strengths: ______________________________

Other information: ______________________________

Next steps/plan: ______________________________

Sample Questionnaire

Name: ______________________ Date: ______________________

Age/birth date: ______________________ Race: ______________________

Gender and pronouns: ______________________ School: ______________________

Legal guardian: ______________________ Referral source: ______________________

Who is present for the interview? ______________________

Presenting Concerns

Client's understanding of the concerns: ______________________

____

Guardian's understanding of concerns: ______________________

____

When did these issues begin? ______________________

Impact on home life: ______________________

Impact on school: ______________________

Impact on social settings: ______________________

Additional impact: ______________________

Reason for seeking support now: ______________________

Current life stressors: ______________________

Safety/Risk Assessment

Current thoughts of harm to self or others? ______________________

Current behavior of harm to self or others? ______________________

Plan, means, or intent to harm self? ______________________

Plan, means, or intent to harm others? ______________________

Suicidal thoughts? ______________________

Suicidal plan, means, or intent? ______________________

Additional information: ______________________

____

Family History

Cultural information: ______

Where was the client born? ______

Where does the client currently live? ______

Other places the client has lived and dates: ______

______

______

Who lives in the home? ______

______

Parents' marital status: ______

Parents' relationship (amicable, high-conflict, etc.): ______

Custody arrangement: ______

Information about adoption, foster placements, etc.: ______

______

______

Information about siblings: ______

How is discipline handled? ______

Family mental health history: ______

Additional relevant family information: ______

______

______

Mental Health History

Previous treatment: ______

______

Inpatient treatment: ______

______

Previous diagnoses: ______

Additional information: ______

______

Developmental History

Maternal health issues during pregnancy: ___

Maternal stressors during pregnancy: ___

Pregnancy duration: ___ Length of labor: ___

Birth weight: ___ Type of birth: ___

Health issues at birth: ___

Health issues in infancy: ___

Age when client: ___ Crawled ___ Walked ___ Spoke ___ Spoke in sentences ___

Toilet training information: ___

Additional information: ___

___

Adaptive Functioning

Hygiene skills: ___

Chores client does or helps with: ___

Client's functioning at school: ___

Other functional information: ___

___

Trauma History

Physical abuse: ___

Sexual abuse: ___

Emotional abuse: ___

Physical neglect: ___

Emotional neglect: ___

Family member imprisoned: ___

Domestic violence: ___

Untreated mental illness in the home: ___

Substance dependence in the home: ___

Parent separation/loss/abandonment: ___

Other history of traumatic events: ___

___

Current Medical Information

Primary physician: ______________________________

Current medication, doses, length: ______________________________

Current medical concerns: ______________________________

Additional medical information: ______________________________

____

Medical History

Hospitalizations: ______________________________

____

Surgeries: ______________________________

____

Health concerns/diagnoses: ______________________________

____

Medical symptoms without a diagnosis: ______________________________

____

History of head trauma: ______________________________

Allergies: ______________________________

Educational History

Current school/grade: ______________________________

Previous schools: ______________________________

____

IEP/504/accommodations: ______________________________

Repeated grades: ______________________________

Current grades: ______________________________

Favorite and least favorite subject? ______________________________

School behavior: ______________________________

School concerns: ______________________________

Additional information: ______________________________

____

Employment History

Current job: ______________________________

Previous jobs: ______________________________

Concerns related to work: ______________________________

____

Additional information: ______________________________

____

Social History

Current supports: ______________________________

Close friends: ______________________________

How does the client develop and maintain friendships? ______________________________

____

What kind of friends does the client choose? ______________________________

____

What do conflicts look like? ______________________________

____

Additional information: ______________________________

____

Substance Use

Has client ever had caffeine? ______________________________

Has client ever tried alcohol? ______________________________

Has client ever tried nicotine (vaping or smoking)? ______________________________

Has client ever tried cannabis? ______________________________

Has client ever tried another drug, and if so, what? ______________________________

For any substance client has tried, provide information about first age of use, frequency of use, and amount: ______________________________

____

____

Any history of blackouts? ______________________________

Has client ever required medical attention for substance use? ______________________________

____

Has tolerance for a substance improved over time? ____________________

Additional information: ____________________

Legal History

Has client ever been arrested? ____________________

When and what for? ____________________

Any pending charges: ____________________

Any convictions, probation, jail time, etc.: ____________________

Additional information: ____________________

Client Interests

Extracurricular activities: ____________________

Hobbies: ____________________

Additional information: ____________________

Strengths

Self-identified strengths: ____________________

Parent- or guardian-identified strengths: ____________________

Additional information: ____________________

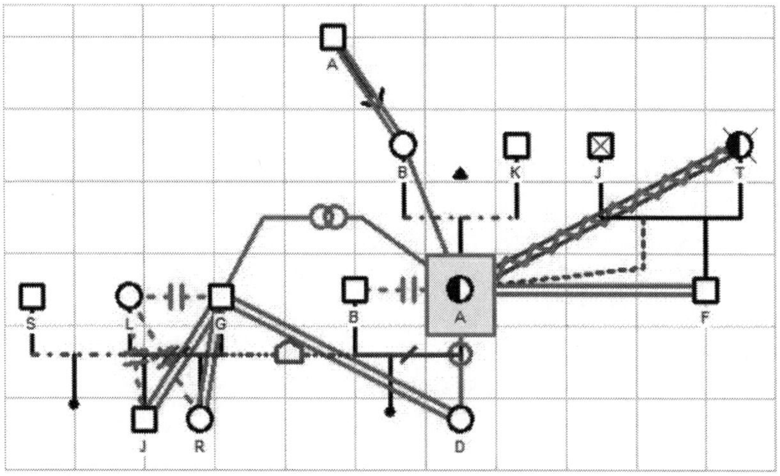

Image 4.1 Sample Genogram
Created with GenPro at https://genopro.com/

Sample Minor Confidentiality Agreement

Date:

This document outlines the agreements around confidentiality and its limitations for [Client's] therapy. [Client] and [List guardian or guardians present and involved in the agreement] understand that [Client] needs to feel safe sharing with their therapist in order to progress in treatment, and [Guardian(s)] might need certain information to ensure [Client's] physical and mental well-being. As such, all parties agree to the following:

1. [Client's] therapist is legally required to report certain information due to certain laws around their profession. [Detail mandated reporting and confidentiality limitations applicable to your jurisdiction here.]
2. If [Client] shares a conflict with the therapist involving family members or peers, and the therapist does not have concerns for [Client's] safety, the therapist will only share these details with [Guardian(s)] with [Client's] expressed permission.
3. Due to [Client's] past overdose and hospitalization related to opiate use, [Guardian(s)] have expressed concern about potential relapse and the dangers of possible future overdose. Because of this, if [Client] discloses drug use to the therapist, this information will be disclosed to [Guardian(s)].
4. [Client] has stated that they want to work on reducing self-harm behaviors but are concerned about [Guardian(s)] reaction to learning that they have cut themselves. [Client] agrees to share self-harm behavior with the therapist if and when it occurs, and [Guardian(s)] understand that, unless there is concern that [Client] requires or will require medical treatment, this will be kept confidential so that [Client] can explore triggers for this behavior and preventative coping skills in a safe environment.

Since [Client's] needs, concerns, and symptoms may change, this agreement can be updated at any time, but the therapist will notify [Client] of any changes to the limits of their privacy in sessions before a change is implemented.

All parties sign below to indicate that they will adhere to this confidentiality agreement. The therapist will only disclose information with [Client's] permission or under the terms detailed above. [Guardian(s)] agree not to request information about [Client's] sessions outside of these terms.

Therapist Name: ______________________________

Therapist Signature: ______________________________

Client Name: ______________________________

Client Signature: ______________________________

Guardian Name: ______________________________

Guardian Signature: ______________________________

Guardian Name: ______________________________

Guardian Signature: ______________________________

Glossary of Terms

adaptive functioning: A person's ability to use skills to survive and thrive in their environment, including aspects like self-care, hygiene, and domestic tasks.

assent: Agreement or approval. In mental health and medical settings, clients who are not able to provide their own consent to care (for example, minor clients) agree to engage in treatment, while their guardian provides formal consent.

consent: Formal permission or agreement for treatment. For minor clients, this is given by the person who has custody or guardianship.

developmental history: An individual's history of growth starting before birth and including information about achieving milestones, learning, and building skills.

diagnostic interview: Typically done in the first session, an in-depth interview during which the provider gathers information about the client's history, symptoms, and other areas.

epigenetic: The way that environment affects and changes an individual's genetic expression.

genogram: A diagram using various symbols to illustrate someone's family members, relations, relationships, and medical and psychological history.

identifying information: Information used to identify an individual, such as name, age, et cetera.

informed consent: A formal document detailing the potential benefits and risks of seeking mental health services, signed by the legal guardian of a client indicating that they understand the service provided.

intake: A first appointment for services.

presenting concern: The specific reason or reasons someone is seeking services.

triggering: When something causes significant emotional distress, usually because of an association to a traumatic memory.

Works Cited

Barsky, A. E. (2022). Sexuality- and gender-inclusive genograms: Avoiding heteronormativity and cisnormativity. *Journal of Social Work Education*, *58*(2), 379–389. https://doi.org/10.1080/10437797.2020.1852637

Berger, S. L., Kouzarides, T., Shiekhattar, R., & Shilatifard, A. (2009). An operational definition of epigenetics. *Genes & Development*, *23*(7), 781–783.

Felitti, V. J., Anda, R. F., Nordenberg, D., Williamson, D. F., Spitz, A. M., Edwards, V., Koss, M. P., & Marks, J. S. (1998). Relationship of childhood abuse and household dysfunction to many of the leading causes of death in adults. *American Journal of Preventive Medicine*, *14*(4), 245–258. https://doi.org/10.1016/S0749-3797(98)00017-8

Keith, C. (2013). *Sexual & gender diversity genograms: A tool to transcend hetero-, cis-, and mono-normativity in practice*. www.slideshare.net/SpectraWorkshops/queer-genograms-workshop-poly-conf

CHAPTER 5

DIAGNOSES

You've finished the intake appointment and documented all the necessary information. Before you sign off, though, you have to input a diagnosis for your client. But which diagnosis is most accurate and appropriate? We often have to input a diagnostic code right after meeting the client. You might feel like you don't know your client well enough to determine their diagnosis, or they might report symptoms that don't quite fit into one category. You also need to document why you assigned your diagnosis. How should you include this information?

What Is a Diagnosis?

A diagnosis is the specific term assigned to a client indicating that their symptoms meet a specific set of criteria. Currently, most therapists use either the *Diagnostic and Statistical Manual of Mental Disorders, 5th Edition, Text Revision* (DSM-5-TR) or the *International Classification of Diseases, Eleventh Revision* (ICD-11). These resources contain detailed information about various conditions and the criteria someone must meet to be diagnosed with that disorder.

The DSM-5-TR was created by the American Psychiatric Association and details the diagnostic criteria, research base, and prevalence of various mental health diagnoses (American Psychiatric Association, 2022). The ICD-11 includes information about mental health diagnoses as well as information about medical conditions (ICD-11 & World Health Organization, 2019/2021).

Disorders listed in both the DSM and ICD have significant overlap and are very similar, though they are not identical. Check with your employer to make sure you are using the appropriate resource for your practice and reference the criteria each time you make a diagnosis to ensure that your diagnosis is appropriate for the client.

How Do You Determine a Diagnosis?

When I was a child, I contracted strep throat several times. I always knew when I was feeling sick – I felt tired or down, possibly feverish, and I would get the telling sore throat. My parents knew that this was a signal to take me to the doctor, who would determine my diagnosis and provide appropriate treatment based on that. The doctor used a swab to collect a sample from my throat, sent that sample to the lab, and the test results showed definitively whether or not I had strep throat.

Mental health diagnoses can be a bit trickier. Unfortunately, there is no simple swab test for Major Depressive Disorder or ADHD. As noted in Chapter 4, part of your diagnostic interview includes asking about specific symptoms and pulling together information about a possible diagnosis from

DOI: 10.4324/9781003316442-5

that. You might also use assessments to determine whether or not a client's symptoms are clinically significant.

Whatever information you are using, it is important to document how you concluded that a client has the diagnosis. Most mental health diagnoses, once they are a part of someone's medical record, are there forever. It can be difficult to get an inaccurate diagnosis removed, which can be a barrier for treatment if someone faces stigma as a result of that diagnosis or is offered treatment options that are not indicated based on their actual presentation.

What Does a Diagnosis Include?

In the text revision of the fourth edition of the DSM (DSM-IV-TR), clients were assigned a multiaxial diagnosis consisting of five components (American Psychiatric Association, 2000):

- Axis I: Mental health diagnoses, including substance use disorders.
- Axis II: Personality disorders and intellectual disabilities (which were diagnosed as Mental Retardation at the time).
- Axis III: Medical conditions that the client has.
- Axis IV: Psychosocial or environmental factors contributing to the person's mental health.
- Axis V: Global Assessment of Functioning (GAF) score.

Currently, diagnoses are not broken into the different axes. Instead, we simply list the client's diagnoses. A mental health provider would include the diagnosis or diagnoses that previously were included in Axis I and Axis II but not medical conditions (though it is important to note any medical conditions a client has as a part of a thorough social history – see Chapter 4).

While insurance companies typically only cover treatment for condition diagnoses (those that were previously listed on Axes I and II), you can additionally include Z Codes, or indicators of environmental factors and stressors that the client is currently dealing with. If the entity paying for treatment does not require an official diagnosis, you can diagnose only Z Codes, but most insurances will only cover "official" diagnosis codes and not Z Codes. This might be most appropriate for a client who wants to develop appropriate coping skills or a couple coming to work on their communication if they do not technically meet criteria for another diagnosis. Z Codes are currently listed along with other diagnostic codes.

The GAF score was a number on a scale from 1 to 100 indicating a client's current level of functioning. Basically, you were estimating the client's total level of impairment with this score. Some providers struggled with ambiguity with the GAF score. While we do not typically use GAF scores anymore, you can detail impairments by noting the severity of a diagnosis or including information about impairments in the Mental Status Examination (MSE) (see Chapter 7). The MSE provides insight into the client's functioning and current status in specific ways rather than an overall score.

When assigning a diagnosis, include the diagnostic code, the name of the diagnosis, and any qualifiers. For example, when diagnosing Post-Traumatic Stress Disorder, you can indicate whether the diagnosis is Acute, Chronic, or Unspecified.

In addition to the diagnosis and diagnostic code, include a diagnostic impression that details your rationale for assigning the diagnosis. This would include specific symptoms the client is experiencing, the severity, how long these symptoms have been present, and how they are manifesting in the client's day-to-day life.

What If I'm Not Sure?

In the United States, many people use health insurance to cover the cost of mental health treatment. Unfortunately, most insurers require that the provider assign a diagnosis by the end of the intake interview in order to provide coverage for services. This puts a lot of pressure on you as a provider to determine a diagnosis with limited information – no matter how thorough your intake interview, how well can you really know someone after one hour?

Many of the diagnoses listed in the DSM and ICD include "Unspecified" types. For example, your client may endorse anxiety symptoms that do not quite meet the criteria for Generalized Anxiety Disorder, Social Anxiety Disorder, or Panic Disorder, but their symptoms do cause enough distress that they are seeking treatment. You have the option to diagnose Unspecified Anxiety Disorder, note what information is missing to grant a more specific diagnosis, and detail the symptoms disclosed.

The diagnostic criteria for Unspecified Anxiety Disorder, according to the DSM-5-TR, states: "This category applies to preventions in which symptoms and characteristics of an anxiety disorder cause clinically significant distress or impairment . . . but do not meet the full criteria for any of the disorders in the anxiety disorders diagnostic class. The unspecified anxiety disorder category is used in situations in which the clinician chooses *not* to specify the reason that the criteria are not met for a specific anxiety disorder" (American Psychiatric Association, 2022).

The "Unspecified" categories have similar criteria in that they all indicate when a client has symptoms not better accounted for by a more specific disorder.

Similarly, many chapters in the DSM include a category of an "Other Specified" diagnosis. This again means that the client did not seem to meet the full criteria for another specific anxiety disorder, and the provider is detailing specific symptoms noted. Continuing to use anxiety disorders as an example, the criteria for Other Specified Anxiety Disorder states: "This category applies to presentations in which symptoms characteristic of an anxiety disorder that cause clinically significant distress or impairment . . . predominate but do not meet the full criteria for any of the disorders in the anxiety disorders diagnostic criteria. The Other Specified Anxiety Disorder category is used in situations in which the clinician chooses to communicate the specific reason that the presentation does not meet the criteria for any specific anxiety disorder" (American Psychiatric Association, 2022).

Each chapter that includes the option for an "Other Specified" diagnosis includes examples of what a provider might specify, but the provider can also include their own specifications.

Provisional Diagnoses and Rule-Outs

Maybe your client or their guardian reports symptoms that seem to meet the diagnostic criteria for a disorder, but you want to gather more data to know for sure. Maybe they have displayed symptoms for five months, but the diagnostic criteria for that disorder states symptoms must persist for at least six months. Maybe your client is unable to communicate directly about their symptoms, and so you are primarily relying on the guardian for this information.

For these and many other reasons, clinicians often assign diagnoses *provisionally*. A provisional diagnosis indicates that a client seems to meet criteria for a diagnosis, and they display many of the diagnostic criteria, but you need more time, information, observations, et cetera, before you can confidently assign the diagnosis. A provisional diagnosis is one that you plan to confirm in the future once you have gathered the needed information.

Similarly, some clinicians assign *rule-out* diagnoses. A rule-out diagnosis means that the provider wants additional assessment in order to either confirm or rule out that the client meets criteria for that diagnosis. The difference is that a provisional diagnosis suggests that the client exhibits many of the symptoms presented, and a rule-out indicates that more information is needed before you can determine whether these symptoms are present.

Rule-out diagnoses and provisional diagnoses can be helpful in determining what additional assessments the client needs and can provide a starting point for a treatment plan before you have gotten to know the client well enough to assign an official diagnosis. They can also be beneficial if the client enters treatment during a crisis and baseline information about their symptoms is not available.

Specifiers

Some diagnostic categories also include optional specifiers. The specifiers can allow you to be more specific about how the diagnosis presents for your client and what symptoms they are dealing with. This can be helpful when explaining the diagnosis to the client or their guardian, or if other members of a treatment team will be using your diagnosis for treatment-planning purposes.

Depressive disorders, for example, can include optional specifiers such as "with anxious distress" (the client experiences anxious symptoms as a component of their depressive episodes), "with seasonal pattern" (when the depressive symptoms consistently occur during a certain time of year), or "with psychotic features" (the depressive episodes are accompanied by delusions or hallucinations) (American Psychiatric Association, 2022).

Diagnoses can also be specified as being in partial or full remission. If your client met criteria for a diagnosis but no longer meets criteria following treatment, you may update their chart to reflect that they are in remission and no longer exhibiting symptoms. This can be appropriate if you are writing a termination note (see Chapter 8 for an example of this) to indicate that a client has stopped meeting criteria for the diagnosis that brought them in for treatment.

Childhood Diagnoses

Many of the diagnoses listed in the DSM have specific criteria about what age a client needs to be before the diagnosis can be assigned, but the client's chart typically will allow providers to insert a diagnosis even if the client is not in that age range. Because of this, we have a responsibility to double-check this information before assigning a diagnosis that might not be age appropriate. For example, Disruptive Mood Dysregulation Disorder cannot be diagnosed prior to age 6 and must have symptom onset prior to age 18. If a client is five and one-half years old, you may note the criteria and diagnose provisionally or assign another mood disorder, then re-assess when the client is old enough for the diagnosis.

Some diagnoses are extremely rare in early childhood but not impossible. For example, the typical age of onset for bipolar disorder is around age 20 (Duffy et al., 2019). While it is not impossible for a younger child to develop bipolar disorder, this is exceedingly rare. Consider whether another diagnosis better explains the client's symptoms, and only assign this diagnosis in a child if you have sufficient evidence that they truly meet the criteria.

Similarly, while some diagnoses can be made in adolescence, it is challenging to determine whether the client fully meets the diagnostic criteria when they are that young. For example, the current DSM allows for some personality disorders to be diagnosed starting at age 14. However, personality disorders are defined as "an enduring pattern of inner experience and behavior that deviates markedly from the expectations of the individual's culture, is pervasive and inflexible, has an onset in adolescence or early adulthood, is stable over time, and leads to distress or impairment" (American Psychiatric Association,

2022). What is an "enduring pattern" that is "pervasive and inflexible" when an individual is 14 years old? How can you be certain they are not going through a temporary phase? Clinicians must use caution when assigning a diagnosis and make sure they are confident that the child or adolescent meets those diagnostic criteria in order to prevent inaccurate diagnoses.

Diagnoses that are typically appropriate for children and teens include: Attention-Deficit/Hyperactivity Disorder, Autism Spectrum Disorder, Anxiety, Depressive or Mood Disorders, Trauma Disorders, Conduct and Impulse Control-Related Disorders, and Adjustment Disorders. Your diagnostic impression should include details about why you assigned the diagnosis and justification for how the client meets the diagnostic criteria. Keep in mind, additionally, that some types of clinicians are not permitted to make certain diagnoses. (For example, in some of the United States, Licensed Professional Counselors cannot diagnose neurodevelopmental disorders like ADHD and autism.) Make sure that you are practicing within your scope when you assign a diagnosis.

Even if a diagnosis can be diagnosed in childhood, though, most diagnoses have a minimum age before which they can be diagnosed. For example, a client must be at least six years old to be diagnosed with Disruptive Mood Dysregulation Disorder and four years old to be diagnosed with ADHD (American Psychiatric Association, 2022). Reactive Attachment Disorder can be diagnosed as early as nine months.

Additional Diagnostic Considerations

Remember that many diagnoses remain in a client's medical record even if you later decide that you were wrong, and they never had the diagnosis to begin with. It is unfair, but if you diagnose a child with Oppositional Defiant Disorder (ODD) and later realize that their behavior was related to a trauma disorder instead, ODD remains on the medical record. If services are billed to insurance, the insurance company keeps a record of the diagnosis as well, so an update to your records will not remove the diagnosis from their records with the insurance company.

Additionally, misdiagnosis can lead to a client receiving treatment that is not appropriate for their needs. If the parent or guardian wants to consider medication for their child, an incorrect diagnosis means that child might be prescribed medication that is not appropriate for them to take. This is why it is often preferable to be overly cautious when assigning a diagnosis.

Remember that a client can meet criteria for multiple diagnoses, but they do not necessarily have several different conditions. If, for example, you notice that a client exhibits both depressive and anxious symptoms, they may meet criteria for a mood disorder and a separate anxiety disorder. However, if the anxious symptoms only occur in the context of a depressive episode, you might diagnose a depressive disorder with the specifier "with anxious distress." Providers aim to be accurate and thorough, as well as concise, when assigning diagnoses.

Providers must also be aware of any cultural considerations to a diagnosis. If a behavior is culturally appropriate, it is not a symptom. For example, clients from cultures where "family business" is not discussed outside of the home can be mislabeled as "resistant" because they are not opening up to the therapist. Be sure to consider any relevant cultural factors when considering a diagnosis.

Similarly, providers need to keep in mind that much of the diagnostic criteria listed in the DSM is based on research of predominantly white, Western cultures. This can impact access to care because BIPOC clients are more likely to be misdiagnosed than white clients. This is particularly prevalent with autism (Aylward et al., 2021) but occurs with many other diagnoses as well.

Finally, providers must consider their own potential biases. While racial biases are most prominent among white providers, clinicians of all races have shown implicit bias toward white clients due to systemic racism and white supremacy (Johnson, 2020). This can manifest, for example, as Black children being more frequently diagnosed with Oppositional Defiant Disorder rather than ADHD or a trauma disorder compared to white children (Day, 2002).

While no provider is immune from misdiagnosing a client, an awareness of potential biases and common misconceptions can help ensure that clients receive appropriate care.

Is a Diagnosis Always Necessary?

In the United States, insurance companies typically require that a condition be diagnosed in order for them to cover the cost of treatment. However, if a client is paying out-of-pocket for their sessions, you could have the option to not grant a diagnosis or to only diagnose Z Codes that are based on the client's current life stressors. Z Codes are at much lower risk for misdiagnosis, as they relate to specific facts that can be confirmed. For instance, Z65.5 indicates "Disruption of Family by Separation or Divorce." Your client's parents are either separated or together, and it is easy to confirm this information.

Even if the entity covering your client's sessions does not require a diagnosis, you might still assign a diagnosis if it is appropriate and if you have sufficient evidence indicating that the client meets the diagnostic criteria for that disorder.

Regardless of payer coverage, it is never appropriate to assign a diagnosis if you know that your client does not meet the diagnostic criteria.

Diagnostic Impressions

The diagnostic impression consists of two parts: The diagnosis (or diagnoses) you assign and their corresponding code (or codes), and information justifying why you assigned this diagnosis. In some cases, you might be working from a diagnosis assigned by another provider. For example, if you are unable to diagnose ADHD but the client completed an evaluation with a qualified provider, you can list the ADHD diagnosis and note that you are going by that evaluation in your diagnostic paragraph. That would look like this:

F90.2 Attention-Deficit/Hyperactivity Disorder: Combined Presentation

Client was evaluated by [Provider name] on [Date of report]. [Provider name] indicates that, per the results of that evaluation, the client meets the diagnostic criteria for ADHD: Combined Presentation.

However, if you are writing a diagnosis that you assigned, the diagnostic impression will be much longer and more thorough, including what symptoms you observed; what symptoms the client disclosed to you; what symptoms a parent, guardian, or other source disclosed to you; and what symptoms you reviewed in additional records, if any were provided.

Who Sees the Diagnostic Impression?

In most cases, the parent or other legal guardian of a minor client has the right to view their diagnostic impression. It is typically appropriate to inform the guardian when you diagnose their child, and education and information about the diagnosis can help the guardian make appropriate parenting choices for the child. Knowing the child's diagnosis can also help them understand the child's symptoms when the child is having a hard time.

If you are billing insurance, the insurance claim must include a diagnostic code but does not include the overall diagnostic impression. Sometimes the insurance company will request additional information or audit you client's account, so it is always possible that they will see the entire diagnostic impression.

If you are part of a child's treatment team, often their primary physician or pediatrician will see the diagnostic impression as well, which can help them make any appropriate recommendations about medication or other therapies that might benefit the child. If the child is diagnosed with ADHD, autism, or a learning disorder, the guardian may authorize you to share the diagnosis with the child's school so that they can request appropriate accommodations.

Depending on the child's age, they might not see their diagnostic impression. For example, a young, elementary-aged child might not be able to understand clinical language included in the document. However, teens might have the right to read their diagnostic impression depending on your jurisdiction. Additionally, when a child grows up, they have the right to access their medical records. Always assume that your client will see what you have written about them in their chart.

Even if a child is too young to understand the diagnostic impression, they can benefit from knowing what their diagnosis is and having it explained to them in an age-appropriate way. The parent or guardian can do this on their own, or they might ask that this be something you do together as part of the child's treatment plan. Sometimes children's books and other resources can help tell a child about their diagnosis. For example, *All Dogs Have ADHD* is a fun, informative book that explains what it means to have ADHD in a way that young children can understand (Hoopmann, 2009).

Samples

Next, you will find two sample diagnostic impressions. One includes an open narrative where you note specific symptoms and their presentation in paragraph format. The other uses a checkbox format that allows you to list the symptoms of a particular diagnosis and check which criteria your client presents with. Both include space to note additional information needed and rule-outs as appropriate.

While finding your personal style is an important part of clinical documentation, the diagnostic impression might vary depending on the situation. If your client comes to their intake in an acute crisis, it is likely not appropriate to assign a diagnosis unrelated to that crisis, as they may not be presenting with typical symptoms. When you assign an "Unspecified" diagnosis, there is not a long list of diagnostic criteria to review, and so a narrative format may be a better fit. On the other hand, when diagnosing a specific mood or anxiety disorder, it is important to document the specific symptoms and demonstrate that your client fully meets those criteria. It can also be important to note other symptoms that did not lead to an additional diagnosis and why the diagnostic criteria were not met.

I encourage you to use whichever format best relays this information about a given client, especially if you work in a setting where you are on a treatment team and other providers will see your diagnostic impression. This will allow them to fully understand which symptoms led to that diagnosis.

If you use the checkbox format, it can be helpful to pre-make symptom lists for diagnoses that you see often. This way, you can paste the template into your notes and simply go through and check off the applicable boxes rather than having to enter them manually every time.

Sample Diagnostic Impression: Open Narrative

Diagnoses: F41.1 Generalized Anxiety Disorder

F32.9 Unspecified Depressive Disorder

Z Codes: Z55.9 Problems Related to Education

Narrative: The parent reports that the client is "always worrying" and expresses nervousness most days. The client reportedly cannot fall asleep at night by herself due to feeling "afraid," though she is unable to articulate a specific source of the fear. She appears restless and is often tired as a result of the worrying behavior, which she seems unable to control. Symptoms were observed in the intake session, with the client moving around the room, fidgeting, and exhibiting muscle tension beyond what is a typical response to an unfamiliar situation. Symptoms have been present for approximately one year. Client's presentation at intake, as well as parent's report of symptoms, meet the diagnostic criteria for Generalized Anxiety Disorder.

Additionally, the client shared that she feels "sad all the time." The guardian has observed negative self-talk and statements like, "I wish I was never born." Both client and guardian were unsure whether these symptoms are episodic or exactly how long they have occurred. As such, Unspecified Depressive Disorder is provisionally diagnosed, as the client reports clinically significant mood issues consistent with depression, but there is not sufficient information to provide a more specific diagnosis.

The parent also reports that the client is struggling in school due to difficulty reading. See the following rule-outs for recommendations regarding additional testing.

Rule-Outs: Specific Learning Disorder: The parent reports that the client is struggling in school due to being behind grade expectations, specifically in reading. Further testing is recommended.

Sample Diagnostic Impression: Open Narrative (Blank)

Diagnoses: ______________________________

____

____

Z Codes: ______________________________

____

____

Narrative: ______________________________

____

____

____

____

____

Rule-Outs: ______________________________

____

____

Sample Diagnostic Impression: Check Boxes

Diagnoses: F90.0 Attention-Deficit/Hyperactivity Disorder: Predominantly Inattentive Presentation

Z Codes: Z62.891 Sibling Rivalry

Diagnostic Criteria: A persistent pattern of inattention that interferes with functioning or development, as characterized by at least six of the following:

Often fails to give close attention to details or makes careless mistakes	X
Often has difficulty sustaining attention to tasks or activities	
Often does not seem to listen when spoken to	X
Often does not follow through on instructions and fails to finish tasks	X
Often has difficulty organizing tasks and activities	X
Often avoids or is reluctant to engage in tasks requiring mental effort	
Often loses things necessary for tasks or activities	X
Is easily distracted	X
Is often forgetful	X
Symptoms present prior to age 12	X
Symptoms present in two or more settings	X
Symptoms interfere with functioning	X
Symptoms not attributed to another diagnosis	X

Rule-Outs:

Sample Diagnostic Impression: Check Boxes (Blank)

Diagnoses: ______________________

____

____

Z Codes: ______________________

____

____

Diagnostic Criteria: ______________________

____

____

____

____

____

____

____

____

____

____

____

____

____

____

____

____

____

____

____

____

Rule-Outs: ______________________

____

____

Glossary of Terms

ADHD: A neurodevelopmental disorder categorized by issues with inattentive and/or hyperactive-impulsive symptoms, with early developmental onset and which impacts functioning in at least two settings.

Adjustment Disorder: A reaction to stressful events or changes in one's life, which can manifest as emotional or behavioral struggles. The reaction is in excess of what would be considered a typical stress response.

Anxiety Disorder: Diagnoses characterized by intense anxious or panic symptoms that are not consistent with appropriate concern for danger.

Autism: A neurodevelopmental disorder categorized by atypical social and communication styles, repetitive thoughts, speech, and/or behaviors, and sensory sensitivities.

Bipolar Disorder: A disorder occurring when an individual experiences manic or hypomanic episodes and possibly depressive episodes.

deferred: When there is not sufficient evidence to make a diagnosis, the provider may defer their diagnosis to another professional with more information or assessment training.

Depression: A disorder characterized by low moods, negative thoughts, feelings of sadness, and loss of interest in things you previously enjoyed.

diagnosis: The identified name of a disorder, granted when an individual meets the symptom criteria.

diagnostic code: The written indicator of a specific diagnosis.

diagnostic impression: Information about a client's specific diagnosis or diagnoses as well as the justification for the diagnosis.

differential: The process that a provider uses to differentiate two similar diagnoses and determine which best fits the client's presenting symptoms.

Global Assessment of Functioning Score: GAF score, a way to assess an individual's level of functioning that is no longer used.

Impulse Control Disorder: A set of disorders marked by chronic inability to regulate impulses and self-control that is not developmentally appropriate.

Mood Disorder: Depressive disorders.

Multiaxial Diagnosis: A way of conceptualizing a client's diagnoses that was used in the DSM-IV-TR.

Neurodevelopmental Disorder: Disorders that can impair communication, behavior, cognition, and other development that result from atypical brain development, with onset during early childhood.

Oppositional Defiant Disorder: A type of impulse control disorder marked by defiance, hostility, oppositionality, and noncompliance.

other specified: When a client's presentation does not fully meet criteria for another disorder, and the clinician is specifying the nature of their symptoms.

Personality Disorder: "An enduring pattern of inner experience and behavior that deviates markedly from the expectations of the individual's culture, is pervasive and inflexible, has an onset in adolescence or early adulthood, is stable over time, and leads to distress or impairment" (American Psychiatric Association, 2022).

provisional: A diagnosis that has been assigned based on the client's current presentation, but the provider notes that they may not always meet that criteria and will update the diagnosis later.

remission: A client previously met criteria for a diagnosis but no longer meets criteria

rule-out: A client shows some symptoms of a diagnosis, but further assessment is needed to confirm whether they can be diagnosed.

trauma: An experience that is distressing or disturbing.

unspecified: When a client exhibits symptoms that do not fully meet the criteria of a specific diagnosis, and the clinician does not indicate the specific symptoms displayed.

Z Code: A group of codes used to indicate environmental factors that can contribute to a client's mental status and well-being.

Works Cited

American Psychiatric Association. (2000). *Diagnostic and statistical manual of mental disorders* (4th ed., Text Revision). American Psychiatric Association.

American Psychiatric Association. (2022). *Diagnostic and statistical manual of mental disorders* (5th ed., Text Revision). American Psychiatric Association.

Aylward, B. S., Gal-Szabo, D. E., & Taraman, S. (2021). Racial, ethnic, and sociodemographic disparities in diagnosis of children with autism spectrum disorder. *Journal of Developmental & Behavioral Pediatrics, 42*(8), 682–689. https://doi.org/10.1097/DBP.0000000000000996

Day, J. (2002). *The effect of race on the diagnosis of oppositional defiant disorder*. ERIC.

Duffy, A., Goodday, S., Keown-Stoneman, C., & Grof, P. (2019). The emergent course of bipolar disorder: Observations over two decades from the Canadian high-risk offspring cohort. *American Journal of Psychiatry, 176*(9), 720–729. https://doi.org/10.1176/appi.ajp.2018.18040461

Hoopmann, K. (2009). *All dogs have ADHD*. Jessica Kingsley Publishers.

International classification of diseases, eleventh revision (ICD-11), & World Health Organization (WHO). (2019/2021). *Licensed under creative commons attribution-noderivatives 3.0 IGO license (CC BY-ND 3.0 IGO)*. https://icd.who.int/browse11

Johnson, T. J. (2020). Racial bias and its impact on children and adolescents. *Pediatric Clinics of North America, 67*(2), 425–436. https://doi.org/10.1016/j.pcl.2019.12.011

CHAPTER 6

TREATMENT PLANS

A parent contacts you about starting therapy for their child. They know the child is struggling, and they share what behaviors and emotional issues are causing problems in the child's life. When you ask them what their expected outcome is for therapy, though, they give you a blank look. They say, "I just want my child to feel happy," "I want them to make better choices," or "I wish they would just stop _______." How does that translate into your treatment with the child? How can you, in conjunction with your client and their parent, create an appropriate treatment plan?

What Is a Treatment Plan?

In therapy, a treatment plan contains detailed information about the client's diagnosis, presenting concerns, goals for treatment, and what interventions the therapist will use to treat them. It includes how long therapy may be expected to take, though this is difficult to guess, especially with children who may take a while to build rapport before fully engaging in the presented interventions. You may decide to indicate that the treatment plan is for a pre-set length of time, such as six months, that does not indicate treatment will be *finished* at that time, but rather that you will re-assess the treatment plan at that time. After that time has elapsed, you can re-assess the client's progress toward their goals and determine whether some have been met, whether the client has new goals they want to add, or whether you need to adjust your interventions and approach to better meet the client's needs. If you see clients over long periods of time, it is good practice to regularly review the treatment plan to ensure that the stated goals remain relevant and to document progress (Hutchinson et al., 2008).

When working with children, a treatment plan can include the client's self-identified goals in addition to the goals the parent or guardian brings up. These two sets of goals are not always consistent, as the client might have different ideas about the goal of therapy. Part of developing the treatment plan includes reviewing these differences and ensuring that the client and parent are on the same page about the therapist's priorities and focus in treatment as well as what treatment will look like.

Components of a Treatment Plan

Treatment plan templates vary depending on legal, ethical, and payer requirements. A basic treatment plan includes the presenting problem and the client's goals for treatment. All components of a treatment plan include:

1. **Presenting problem:** What brings the client to treatment? What symptoms or behaviors are they exhibiting, and what is their diagnosis? What is happening right now, or what changed recently, that caused them to seek help at this time compared to a month ago?

DOI: 10.4324/9781003316442-6

2. **People involved in the treatment plan:** Developmental level varies, but most children have some perception that they are coming to therapy and have some idea about the reasons why. You may deem it appropriate to go over the treatment plan with the guardian first, but it is typically appropriate and good practice to talk with the child about their expectations for treatment as well. If you meet with the guardian separately, note this and your rationale for making that decision.
3. **Goals for therapy:** This is the outcome or outcomes that the parent and child want for therapy. You can note which goals are the parent's and which are the child's, as both sets of input are relevant, and it is important to include the child's goals even if they are not "traditional" therapy goals.
4. **Objectives:** More detailed than goals, therapy objectives are the specific outcomes that lead to achieving the therapy goals. A goal is a big-picture, overarching, desired outcome, whereas objectives are more specific ideas of what that progress looks like. Again, the child and parent may have different objectives they want to focus on.
5. **Interventions:** Note what specific interventions the therapist will use in treatment and how those interventions contribute to achieving the treatment goals and objectives. This section can include input from the client and their guardian, but your clinical expertise is relevant here. The average non-therapist will have limited knowledge about what interventions are appropriate. At the same time, collaborate with your client about what is the best fit for their treatment and their comfort level.
6. **Confidentiality:** It is important that all parties involved in treatment are on the same page about confidentiality and privacy in the client's sessions, the limitations to confidentiality, and what information from sessions will and will not be shared with the parent or guardian. This is detailed more specifically in Chapter 4.

What Are Treatment Goals?

Treatment goals are the desired outcomes for therapy. Goals should be achievable, realistic, and individualized for each client. Parents typically have goals for their child's treatment when they request an appointment, though these goals may be vague and not fully defined. The therapist can work with the parent to articulate their goals.

Depending on the client's age, developmental level, and feelings about treatment, they may or may not have their own goals for therapy. A child who asked their parent to bring them to therapy will likely have some idea of what they want from therapy (for example, "I want to not feel so sad all the time"). However, a parent may make an appointment without telling the child their concerns first, or they might schedule therapy even if the child states that they do not want to go. In this case, the child may feel like they have no goals for therapy, or their goal might be "To not come back." This issue will be discussed later in the chapter.

Once clients and their parents have shared their perceived goals for therapy, the therapist helps them craft these ideas into specific, measurable, appropriate treatment goals for the treatment plan.

What Are Treatment Objectives?

Objectives are subsets of the treatment goal. Essentially, the goal is what the client wants to achieve from coming to therapy, and the objectives are the specific tools, skills, and interventions that will be used to achieve those goals (Perkinson, 2012). While the therapist and client work together to craft the specific treatment goals, the treatment objectives might include interventions that the therapist believes will be beneficial.

Informed consent means that clients understand and agree to each intervention before engaging in it. With children and teens, this means explaining the intervention at a developmentally appropriate level and giving them the opportunity to say that they do or do not want to try what the therapist is suggesting. You may query whether the client feels they are not ready for an intervention at this time or whether they think that it will never be appropriate, and you can save an intervention for later in treatment as appropriate.

Treatment objectives can include various things that the therapist knows they can try in therapy with the knowledge that not every objective will end up being used. While clients are the experts on their own lives, the therapist is the expert on what interventions are likely to be effective in achieving the client's treatment goals. The therapist brings objectives and interventions that may be a good fit, and they collaborate with the client in trying out different objectives to determine which ones will be most effective for the individual.

Stepwise Goals

Often, clients and their parents come to treatment with large, long-term goals that might not be immediately accessible. For example, a child with obsessive compulsive disorder is spending several hours each night washing up before bed due to their compulsions. The child or their parent might want the child to be able to complete their bedtime routine in 30 minutes. They have articulated what it will look like when the goal is achieved, but the client is unlikely to be able to move from where they are now to that goal in one leap.

Stepwise goals focus on what the client can reasonably achieve right now based on their current symptoms. In this example, it could mean that a child aims to reduce the time spend in the compulsive behaviors by 15 minutes rather than trying to cut it down completely. Once they can consistently meet the goal as written, they can re-evaluate and adjust their goal one piece at a time until they reach the larger, long-germ goal.

Treatment plans need regular updates to indicate what goals have been met or need to be adjusted. If you are utilizing stepwise goals, you might update with more frequency to reflect the client's progress. You can also list a series of steps and simply input the next step into the treatment plan when one step is met.

What Makes a Good Treatment Goal?

It is both best practice in mental health treatment and a requirement by many payers that treatment goals meet certain criteria. The purpose of the treatment plan is for the client, therapist, and legal guardian (when applicable) to understand the expected outcome of treatment and how the therapist intends to help the client reach this outcome.

As noted previously, clients and parents often come into therapy with vague, general ideas about what they hope to gain from treatment, and the therapist must help them articulate more specific goals. What goes into strong treatment goals?

- **SMART Goals:** SMART goals are treatment goals that are Specific, Measurable, Achievable, Relevant, and Time-Limited. There is strong evidence supporting the efficacy of SMART goals in creating comprehensive treatment plans with agreed-upon, identifiable outcomes (Bowman et al., 2015).
    - **Specific:** In order to know when a goal has been achieved, the goal must be specific. It must indicate exactly what the outcome will look like and what steps must be taken to achieve that outcome. The

client, their parent, and the therapist must all be on the same page with the same understanding of what the goal is and who will take which steps to support achieving the goal.

  - **Measurable:** There need to be methods in place to measure progress toward the goal. This can include screening items or psychological assessments, observation from adults, and feedback from the client about how they are progressing toward the goal.
  - **Achievable:** As previously noted, a client or their parent may have clear ideas about their long-term goals and hopes for treatment. This is great but not always achievable when crafting treatment goals. Goals should be broken down into achievable steps and reflect what the client is capable of based on where they are currently.
  - **Relevant:** Goals should relate directly to the client's priorities and what they want to get out of treatment. Part of developing a treatment plan is helping the client and their parent or guardian get on the same page about what these priorities are and what makes a goal relevant to the client's treatment plan.
  - **Time-Measured:** Payers often require that treatment plans include information about how long treatment will take, and this is part of crafting appropriate SMART goals. This is challenging because we do not always know exactly how long it will take for a client to master various skills, build trust and rapport with their therapist, or experience relief from their symptoms. The time indicated in a treatment plan is an estimate, of course, and you will likely need to revisit this component as you see your client's progress.

- **PACT Goals:** PACT goals are Purposeful, Actionable, Continuous, and Trackable. These goals focus on creating ongoing change and growth, versus SMART goals' emphasis on achievable outcomes. While PACT goals have not been studied as extensively as SMART goals, PACT goals emphasize skill development that a client can continue to use long after termination of treatment. PACT goals have significant strengths but can be more difficult to tailor to requirements by payers. Always be aware of what requirements you must abide by.
  - **Purposeful:** Goals that are purposeful relate to the client's long-term life goals rather than just where they are currently. These goals relate not just to alleviating current symptoms but to helping the client become the person they want to be in the long-term.
  - **Actionable:** Clients' goals need to include steps that are within their control to take. For example, a child might say that their goal is for their teacher to stop giving them detention. An actionable goal would re-frame this as helping the child determine what steps are within their control to reduce their detentions. (Of course, this may also include having the parent advocate for the child with the school!)
  - **Continuous:** When developing PACT goals, help your client determine actions that they can continue taking after they have reached the initial goal. Since this type of goal aims to help the client make life-long changes and continue progressing even after treatment has ended, these goals include things that the client can reasonably continue to do as it continues to help them.
  - **Trackable:** While measurable goals include using outcome-based data showing how the client has progressed, trackable PACT goals again shift the focus to what is within the client's control. For example, instead of completing a screening measure to determine the child's anxiety level, the child instead notes how many days they practiced their muscle relaxation skill.

You might decide that SMART or PACT goals are a better fit for your therapeutic approach, or you might vary which one you implement based on each client's needs. If you use both in your practice, you can keep a template for each on hand and pull whichever is most appropriate for a given client.

What Is "Progress"?

Both SMART and PACT goals have indications of "progress" in therapy. With SMART goals, progress is defined by symptom reduction through the measurable components of the treatment goal. A child struggling with depression whose scores on the Children's Depression Inventory reduce by 25% has shown some progress toward their goal. With PACT goals, a child who engages in hygiene and self-care practices every day has made progress through increasing behaviors that are in their control.

While more difficult to quantify, progress can be internal as well as external. Does the child report more positive mood or higher self-esteem? Do they report that they feel "better"? Do they indicate that they like meeting with the therapist when they previously indicated hesitation about sessions previously? All these things can indicate progress.

Progress is not linear. Sometimes, progress can look like things getting worse before they start to improve (American Psychological Association, 2020). In particular, children who have experienced trauma may have successfully hidden their emotional response for a long time. At the start of therapy, they begin to explore and process difficult and challenging emotions, which can cause an increase in both mood and behavior symptoms before these things start to improve (Han et al., 2021). It is comparable to cleaning a wound so that it can heal – the cleaning process is going to sting, but it is a necessary part of the process. Educate the client and guardian about this possibility so that they are prepared and able to recognize that this can be a sign of progress.

Some payers require documentation of progress and treatment goals that are clearly measurable. Make sure that your measures of progress and treatment goals reflect these requirements. More information about payer requirements can be found in Chapter 3.

Types of Goals

Treatment goals should always be individualized to the client's needs and priorities. Since clients and their parents can struggle with articulating goals, you can explore different categories with them to help flesh out their goals. These categories often include:

1. **Behavior changes:** This can mean either reducing or increasing the frequency of a behavior, like reducing substance use or increasing eating.
2. **Social changes:** This means helping clients with making and keeping friendships or other relationships.
3. **Coping skills:** Clients may want to practice and develop healthy coping skills either in general or to replace unhealthy coping skills.
4. **Regulation skills:** Clients might need to learn how to identify and manage their emotions in a healthy way.

Guardian and Client Input

As noted, the client and their parent or guardian might have different opinions on what the priorities ought to be for treatment. Crafting treatment plans means mediating these differences and creating a plan that reflects your client's priorities as well as the concerns brought up by the parent or guardian. The treatment is for the client, even if the parent is involved. Engagement improves significantly when the client, even a child or teen, has a say in what their therapy will look like (Knutti et al., 2022).

If a client is strongly against going to treatment altogether, it might be most appropriate to discontinue therapy entirely. Since engagement predicts outcomes, a client who outright refuses to attend therapy is unlikely to progress or find therapy beneficial. They will also learn that therapy is something they are forced to do and do not enjoy, so a therapist choosing to discontinue until the client is ready to engage sends the message that therapy is a place where your needs are honored and you are listened to. (Of course, be aware of safety issues and severity of symptoms when making this judgment.)

Since the parent or guardian is usually the one making the appointment, they are likely to be the first to share their expectations and goals for therapy with you. It is important to make sure that the client also has the opportunity to share their goals and priorities. Parents and kids often find, through conversation with the therapist, that their goals are more aligned than they initially thought. Thorough treatment plans will include input from both clients and guardians, as well as have objectives focused on what the client is working on and what the parents are doing to support their progress.

Helping Clients Articulate Treatment Goals

Often, clients and their guardians have only a vague idea of what they want to achieve from therapy. They know that they want to feel "better," but they are unsure what this looks like or what it would mean for them. Questions that can help guide the client and their guardian articulate specific, measurable treatment goals include:

1. How would you know that therapy is "working" or helping?
2. If you woke up tomorrow and things were "better," what would be different than today?
3. What is something that you (your child) do that you wish you could stop doing?
4. How do you know you are having a hard time? How can your parent/guardian tell that you are having a hard time?
5. What does "being bad" or "misbehaving" mean to you?
6. What does "being good" or "behaving well" mean to you?
7. What is something you (your child) doesn't do that you wish you could do?
8. When was the last time you had a really bad day, and what happened?
9. When was the last time you had a really good day, and what happened?
10. What do you wish you could change about your daily routine/schedule?
11. How would you know that you are ready to stop coming to therapy?

Confidentiality

When working with minor clients who have a legal guardian, you not only have to address possible disagreements about treatment goals, but you must consider privacy and confidentiality. Depending on your jurisdiction, your client's parent or guardian may have the right to request and have access to components of the client's record. Parents may also have expectations regarding what the therapist shares with them about the client's sessions. Of course, this can interfere with therapeutic rapport, as the client may struggle to feel comfortable disclosing information if they believe the therapist is going to repeat things to the parent or guardian.

In order for a client to assent to treatment or provide informed consent, they must have accurate information about their confidentiality and its limitations. It is not appropriate for the therapist and guardian to tell the child that the therapist will keep session content confidential if the therapist is sending information about the sessions to the parent. Outside of mandated reporting requirements, therapists have some flexibility in their approach regarding how they handle privacy in their clients' sessions.

Confidentiality of therapy sessions should be addressed when developing the treatment plan, and the parent(s), guardian(s), therapist, and client must all share understanding of how confidentiality will be handled. Some therapists require confidentiality in individual sessions and communicate this to parents, but not all parents are comfortable with this arrangement. Other therapists facilitate and document a conversation between all parties detailing what information will be kept confidential and what information will be shared with the parent or guardian. Of course, the parent may request that certain information be shared that limits the client's comfort sharing in their sessions.

Regardless of what the guardian agrees to at the start of treatment, they may have the legal right to request information from a session even if they previously agreed not to request this information. In this case, the therapist can attempt to use this agreement in the treatment plan to block the request. However, depending on your jurisdiction, the law may ultimately side with the parent and require you to disclose this information.

The client should always be aware of any possible limitations to their confidentiality and privacy in their sessions.

Interventions

Therapy is a flexible process, and new things can come up in a given session that require the provider to adjust their approach or use a tool that they previously did not consider for a given client. If a client presents with a new symptom, provides history information that was not previously known, or states that their goals have changed, we can and ought to adjust our approach in the moment to meet that need.

That being said, treatment plans include information about what interventions a therapist will use in order to help the client reach their goals. Interventions in the treatment plan do not need to include specific activities, worksheets, or a treatment manual, as overly rigid adherence to manualized treatment is often not a good fit in mental health treatment. However, you can list types of interventions you will use in your sessions.

If, for example, your practice emphasizes cognitive behavioral therapy, you may indicate on a treatment plan that you will utilize schema work, cognitive challenging, and ABC analysis. It can help to keep a list of interventions that you use frequently and pull from this each time you write a treatment plan. Some electronic health records include templates that pre-load this list and let clinicians select which interventions they want included on each treatment plan (TherapyNotes, LLC, n.d.). You can always add appropriate interventions as you are trained in a new technique.

Interventions included on this list might include (but of course are not limited to) the following (TherapyNotes, LLC, n.d.):

- Cognitive challenging
- Cognitive reframing
- Communication skills development
- Compliance issues

- Dialectical behavioral therapy
- Exploration of coping patterns
- Exploration of emotions
- Exploration of relationship patterns
- Interactive feedback
- Preventative services
- Psycho-education
- Relaxation/Deep breathing
- Structured problem solving
- Supportive reflection
- Symptom management

Treatment Plans and Play Therapy

Many therapists who work with children utilize some form of play therapy in their sessions. From the outside, non-directive play therapy can look like "just playing" rather than like what one might imagine when picturing a therapy session. If a client's treatment will include play therapy, this must be documented in their treatment plan, including justification for this approach to treatment and its appropriateness for the client. A therapist who uses these interventions needs to understand the evidence base behind play therapy.

First, providers who utilize play techniques such as non-directive play therapy should make sure that they have received appropriate training in the interventions they use in their sessions and follow the research. If a payer audits your records, you can provide evidence for why your approach to treatment with a given client is appropriate.

Research shows that non-directive play therapy can specifically reduce anxiety symptoms in elementary-aged children (Hateli, 2022). A review of 11 studies of child-centered and non-directive play therapies indicates that both approaches can be effective in treating anxiety, depression, trauma, and behavioral disorders (Boghosian, 2022). If a clinician does not take a non-directive or child-centered approach, cognitive behavioral play therapy easily incorporates evidence-based CBT interventions into the play therapy setting (Knell, 2022). As with other forms of therapy, play therapy has comparable treatment outcomes for both in-person and telemental health sessions (Stone, 2021). Finally, research shows that play therapy approaches can be best practice when working with children in a time-limited setting (Ayling et al., 2019).

In short: It is not only appropriate but often best practice to utilize play therapy interventions, including non-directive play therapy, with children.

If you plan to utilize play interventions as part of a client's treatment, note this in their treatment plan along with evidence and clinical justification for these interventions. While it is not appropriate to use a set treatment plan for every client, you may choose to keep notes about the efficacy of play therapy to include in each relevant treatment plan.

Evidence-Based Treatment

When discussing therapy, "evidence-based treatment" refers to treatment that has been shown, through peer-reviewed research, to be effective in treating a specific diagnosis, symptom set, or client demographic. While it is good for therapists to use interventions that have proven effectiveness, there are limitations to developing this evidence base. Most notably, research that goes into creating an evidence base must be conducted in a specific way. How can we prove that this therapeutic intervention is the reason a client showed symptom improvement? Many therapeutic models do not easily lend themselves to research studies.

In addition, in order for an intervention to have a solid evidence base, it must be implemented in a specific way. Again, this is how researchers measure whether or not the intervention is effective because the study controlled the variables. However, especially when working with children, it can be difficult to implement an intervention in the standardized way required in research studies. In order to build rapport with children, providers must exhibit flexibility and adjust as needed for the client to connect with and benefit from the intervention (Marschall, 2022).

Treatment plans can include information about evidence-based treatment and how this will be incorporated into the client's treatment. However, you can also document interventions aimed at building rapport with the client. Since relationship between the client and therapist is the main predictor of therapeutic progress (Clemence et al., 2005), any intervention aimed at building rapport is justifiable in a client's treatment plan.

Payer Requirements

If your clients use their health insurance to help with the cost of care, you must be aware of any payer requirements for the treatment plan. Most Medicaid plans include specific treatment plan requirements. While you may not have to use their template for these treatment plans, you must ensure that the treatment plans that you write are in compliance in the event that you are audited.

Samples

On the next pages, you will find a treatment goal template and case example. You may choose to utilize components of SMART or PACT goals with the template as appropriate. As with the other chapters in this text, you can make these your own and change them to meet your specific needs.

A treatment plan typically includes diagnostic information in addition to the treatment goals. Because diagnosis is covered in Chapter 5, it is not included again here.

Sample Treatment Plan

Client: [CLIENT], 15-year-old female

Participants: [CLIENT], [MOTHER], [FATHER], therapist

Date: 5/30/2024

Treatment Goal 1

[CLIENT] was released from an inpatient substance use program. Client will continue to build on skills learned in the program and maintain sobriety.

Objectives:

1. [CLIENT] will attend individual and group therapy each week.
2. [CLIENT] and the therapist will create a detailed history of [CLIENT]'s substance use to identify triggers and plan relapse prevention.
3. The therapist will provide educational material about substance dependence.
4. [CLIENT] and her parents will practice positive and nonjudgmental communication styles so that [CLIENT] can become comfortable informing them of triggers or risks for relapse.

Treatment Goal 2

While in inpatient treatment, [CLIENT] disclosed that her substance use began after she witnessed her brother's murder. She states that she feels she never grieved this. She and the therapist will treat and work through her trauma.

Objectives:

1. [CLIENT] will develop appropriate coping skills for trauma using a TF-CBT treatment protocol.
2. [CLIENT] and parents will engage in family sessions to process grief together.
3. [CLIENT] will craft a trauma narrative about her experience.

Treatment Goal 3

[CLIENT] will identify healthy coping skills for her emotions and utilize skills effectively to self-regulate.

Objectives:

1. [CLIENT] and therapist will practice various mindfulness, art-based, and body-based coping skills and use affective monitoring tools to determine which are most effective for her.
2. [CLIENT] will practice skills in between sessions and use the Thought Record to keep track of their effectiveness for her to explore in her sessions.

Anticipated Length of Treatment: One year

Frequency of Treatment: Weekly

Confidentiality Agreement: The content of [CLIENT]'s sessions will remain confidential with the exception of any emergent concerns about harm to self or others. [CLIENT]'s parents want to support her in her sobriety and have asked that any reported substance use be shared with them. [CLIENT] states that she understands this concern and agrees with this limitation to confidentiality. This only applies to future substance use. Information disclosed about [CLIENT]'s history will be kept confidential without [CLIENT]'s consent.

Sample Treatment Plan (Blank)

Client: ______________________________

Participants: ______________________________

Date: ______________________________

Treatment Goal 1

____

____

Objectives:

1. ______________________________
2. ______________________________
3. ______________________________

Treatment Goal 2

____

____

Objectives:

1. ______________________________
2. ______________________________
3. ______________________________

Treatment Goal 3

____

____

Objectives:

1. ______________________________
2. ______________________________
3. ______________________________

Anticipated Length of Treatment: ______________________________

Frequency of Treatment: ______________________________

Confidentiality Agreement: ______________________________

____

____

Glossary of Terms

evidence-based: An intervention that has been studied and found to be effective at treating a symptom or diagnosis.

objective: The specific interventions or actions that will be utilized to help the client make progress toward their treatment goals.

PACT Goal: A format for developing therapy goals that emphasizes crafting goals that are Purposeful, Actionable, Continuous, and Trackable.

progress: A client's forward movement toward their treatment goals.

SMART Goal: A format for therapy goals that emphasizes crafting goals that are Specific, Measurable, Achievable, Relevant, and Time-limited.

stepwise goal: A smaller, achievable goal that help a client move closer to their larger goal.

termination: The end of therapy.

therapeutic intervention: A tool or technique used to help the client toward their treatment goals.

treatment: In this context, another term for therapy.

treatment goal: What a client wants to achieve through therapy.

treatment plan: A document that includes detailed information about a client's goals for treatment, the interventions that will be used to achieve these goals, frequency of treatment, and expected length of treatment.

Works Cited

American Psychological Association. (2020). *Understanding psychotherapy and how it works*. American Psychological Association.

Ayling, P., Armstrong, H., & Clark, L. G. (2019). Time-limited play therapy. In *Becoming and being a play therapist*. Routledge.

Boghosian, J. (2022). *An investigation into which techniques of play therapy are most effective across a spectrum of behaviors in children* [thesis]. https://digitalrepository.salemstate.edu/handle/20.500.13013/2625

Bowman, J., Mogensen, L., Marsland, E., & Lannin, N. (2015). The development, content validity and inter-rater reliability of the SMART-goal evaluation method: A standardised method for evaluating clinical goals. *Australian Occupational Therapy Journal, 62*(6), 420–427. https://doi.org/10.1111/1440-1630.12218

Clemence, A. J., Hilsenroth, M. J., Ackerman, S. J., Strassle, C. G., & Handler, L. (2005). Facets of the therapeutic alliance and perceived progress in psychotherapy: Relationship between patient and therapist perspectives. *Clinical Psychology & Psychotherapy, 12*(6), 443–454. https://doi.org/10.1002/cpp.467

Han, H. R., Miller, H. N., Nkimbeng, M., Budhathoki, C., Mikhael, T., Rivers, E., Gray, J., Trimble, K., Chow, S., & Wilson, P. (2021). Trauma informed interventions: A systematic review. *PLoS One, 16*(6), e0252747. https://doi.org/10.1371/journal.pone.0252747

Hateli, B. (2022). The effect of non-directive play therapy on reduction of anxiety disorders in young children. *Counselling and Psychotherapy Research, 22*(1), 140–146. https://doi.org/10.1002/capr.12420

Hutchinson, M., Casper, P., Harris, J., Orcutt, J., & Trejo, M. (2008). *The clinician's guide to writing treatment plans and progress notes*. DADS Adult System of Care. https://bhdp.sccgov.org/sites/g/files/exjcpb716/files/Clinician_Gde_toolkit.pdf

Knell, S. M. (2022). Cognitive behavioral play therapy. In R. D. Friedberg & E. V. Rozmid (Eds.), *Creative CBT with youth*. Springer. https://doi.org/10.1007/978-3-030-99669-7_5

Knutti, K., Björklund Carlstedt, A., Clasen, R., & Green, D. (2022). Impacts of goal setting on engagement and rehabilitation outcomes following acquired brain injury: A systematic review of reviews. *Disability and Rehabilitation, 44*(12), 2581–2590. https://doi.org/10.1080/09638288.2020.1846796

Marschall, A. (2022, April 29). *Trauma-informed CBT for children & adolescents: A clinical playbook for integrating structure with client-centered flexibility*. PESI. https://catalog.pesi.com/item/95888/?_gl=1*o5gqrw*_ga*MTk2NzE5MTg0My4xNjcyMDkzODU2*_ga_JGEX25L44L*MTY3MjA5OTI4NS4yLjEuMTY3MjEwMzEwOS41NS4wLjA.&_ga=2.195487465.41886599.1672093856-1967191843.1672093856

Perkinson, R. R. (2012). The treatment plan. In *Chemical dependency counseling: A practical guide*. Sage Publications.

Stone, J. (Ed.). (2021). *Play therapy and telemental health: Foundations, populations, and interventions*. Routledge.

TherapyNotes, L. L. C. (n.d.). *Quick start: Notes*. TherapyNotes Help Center. https://support.therapynotes.com/article/48-quick-start-notes

CHAPTER 7

MENTAL STATUS EXAMINATIONS

You've just finished a first session with a new child client. The child engaged in various play activities with you and demonstrated some of the behaviors that caused the parent to reach out to you for treatment. How do you conceptualize what the child demonstrated in your mental status examination?

What Is a Mental Status Examination?

All thorough clinical assessments include a mental status examination, or detailed information about the client's current mental capacity. It includes both observation of the client's presentation and behavior and answers to questions about things like current events or simple logic puzzles.

A thorough mental status examination provides essential information in formulating a diagnostic impression. Behaviors and observable symptoms are important in determining the client's level of functioning and current needs. It helps in identifying safety concerns and tells the clinician how the client is perceiving the world around them. In addition to being an essential component of an intake, a brief mental status examination is vital in each session for monitoring symptom changes, regression, and current problems.

There are many standard mental status questions used for adults; however, developmental range makes this more difficult when working with children (Centers for Disease Control and Prevention, 2022). For example, a five-year-old who does not understand why they are in your office does not necessarily raise concerns, as adults often bring children places even though the child does not understand where they are going. On the other hand, it would be concerning if a typical adult does not know why they are in your office or how they got there. A child's understanding of what therapy is, or what a psychological assessment is, will not be as complex or in-depth as an adult's understanding of these concepts (Kazdin, 2003). Similarly, standard mental status questions for adults include directives like, "Name an event that happened recently in the news." Depending on the child's caretakers, they might not have access to this information. For young children, this question might be anxiety-provoking as they might not understand it. For teens, their answer to this question might include a pop culture reference that the therapist may not be familiar with.

Clinicians must consider what is developmentally appropriate for each client. Similarly, children might feel shy or nervous about their appointment and might decline to answer questions. Therapists must consider possible reasons behind a child's behavior or responses in the mental status examination.

When drawing clinical conclusions from a mental status examination, remember that this is a snapshot of the client's mental state at the time of the session. They could be having a rough day, not feel well, or (for first appointments especially) be nervous about meeting with you. Note these considerations when exploring what the mental status examination is telling you.

DOI: 10.4324/9781003316442-7

Parts of the Mental Status Examination

A thorough mental status examination includes many components. Each clinician will tweak the examination based on their style, and there are different ways to gather much of this information. Some parts of the examination might involve observing the client's behavior, while others include specific questions to learn more about the client's functioning (Norris et al., 2016).

A mental status examination might include the following:

1. **Dress/Hygiene:** What is the client wearing? Are their clothes disheveled, wrinkled, neat? How do they appear? Does their hair look brushed? It is important to be mindful of socioeconomic considerations (for example, lower-income clients might wear older clothing, and this does not suggest a functional issue). Additionally, therapists should be aware of cultural considerations related to dress, such as Muslim clients wearing a hijab or Jewish clients wearing a yarmulke.

   - **Telehealth considerations:** You might not be able to gather as much information about the client's hygiene in a telehealth session. However, you can ask them to hold their fingernails to the camera. You can also ask the guardian directly when the client last bathed, brushed their teeth, or did other hygiene tasks. Additionally, in telehealth sessions, you can get more information about the client's living space by seeing the inside of their home. Is it organized? Messy? Does it appear dirty?

   - **Appearance:** Be mindful of the language you use around the client's appearance, as it is easy to impose your own values (FitzGerald & Hurst, 2017). Neutral language is important. Additionally, many mental status examinations for children include information about their physical appearance, which can be unnecessary. For example, I once saw a record that described a child's physical appearance as "attractive," which is an odd thing to say about a child in any context. As you write this component of your mental status examination, ask why you are including information and how it is clinically relevant. Describe what you see rather than using adjectives. Examples of neutral language can include:

     - Instead of "dirty," note if there is something on the client's face or hands, stains on their clothes, or (if in person) there is a noticeable odor.
     - Instead of describing clothing as "casual" or "inappropriate," note what the client is wearing, like a t-shirt, jeans, sweats, et cetera.
     - Instead of noting "eccentric" or "unusual" clothing or behaviors, again, describe specifically what you observe: What colors, patterns, or styles do you see? What do the mannerisms look like?

2. **Eye contact:** Where is the client looking during the session, and what might be the reason for that? Remember that eye contact is not automatically diagnostically relevant, but explore whether the client seems nervous, distracted, or preoccupied.

   - **Telehealth considerations:** In a telehealth session, it is difficult to determine whether the client is looking at you or their self-view, but you can determine whether they are looking around the room or engaged in the session. You can also note whether they seem to be looking at another person in the room who is out of the frame. Be mindful of possible privacy concerns by asking the client where they are, who else is around, and whether or not they feel they have privacy at the time of the session.

   - **Cultural considerations:** In some cultures, avoiding eye contact is an indication of respect. Again, ask yourself why the client might be doing what they are doing.

3. **Orientation:** Typically, orientation refers to whether the client is aware of who they are, where they are, and when they are. (Sometimes this is abbreviated to "oriented times three.") Some also include understanding of why they are in the session.

- **Person:** Ask the client their name. Most children can tell you their first name, but remember that declining to answer could be due to "stranger danger" or discomfort in the session. If the client does not seem oriented to person, document why: Are they confused? Does there seem to be a memory issue? Or do they seem to believe they are someone else?
- **Place:** Ask the client where they are. It can be helpful to ask the parent or guardian prior to the session what they have told the child and compare the child's response to this information. If they are not oriented to place, document where they believe they are and how you know that this is due to disorientation rather than imaginative play or developmentally appropriate understanding of the appointment.
- **Time:** Bear in mind that many young children will not necessarily know what day it is. It can be more appropriate to ask what season it is or what day of the week versus focusing on a specific date. If the client is not oriented to time, again, note how you can tell and observe whether this is developmentally appropriate.
- **Purpose:** Again, check with the parent or guardian before the session and see what the client was told about the appointment. Some children tell me that they are here for "a doctor's appointment," while others say that I am there to "help with my feelings." What response is developmentally appropriate? Additionally, what does the parent's approach to talking about the session tell you about the family's communication style?

4. **Speech:** Is the client's vocabulary consistent with their age and developmental level? Do they have difficulty finding words? Do they speak with a lisp? Do they curse, and is this developmentally typical? Did the way they spoke with you change over the course of the session? Is English the child's first language, and is another language primarily spoken in the home? These are all important considerations.
5. **Attention, focus, and memory:** This category of the mental status examination is significantly affected by the client's age and developmental level. One reason parents of very young children struggle with knowing when to seek assessment and support for attention issues is that developmentally typical children do not have a long attention span (Centers for Disease Control and Prevention, 2022). Note what, if any, aspects of the client's attention and focus are outside of a developmentally typical range. Try to discern whether the client is losing focus or avoiding a question that they might prefer not to answer (and keep in mind that "avoidant" does not mean that they are being "difficult" – they simply might not feel comfortable discussing a certain topic and do not know how to articulate this). The same goes for assessing the client's memory: Do they not remember, or do they feel uncomfortable discussing a topic with you? You also want to explore both recent and remote memory: A client might struggle to remember what occurred earlier that day but have a strong memory of a vacation from a year ago, or they might struggle with long-term memories but have detailed memories of what happened in the days just before the appointment. Here are examples of how to assess for attention, focus, and memory.

   - **Attention:** How well can the client attend to something? If you are engaging in play, let the client direct part or all of a session. How frequently are they changing activities? Does their play include a narrative arc, and if so, is it consistent, or do they change stories frequently? You can also assess this through talk by allowing the client to speak about something that is important to them. Do they stick to the topic or bounce around? Do they jump between somewhat related topics? How do they respond if you redirect them back to the original topic? In your notes, document length of time that the client was able to remain on task or stick to one topic.
   - **Focus:** How well can the client stay engaged in an activity or topic as directed by you, the therapist? You might not be able to assess this if a client feels angry and does not want to do what you asked or struggles to engage due to anxiety. This can be assessed by having the client draw a specific picture at your request, play a game you have chosen, or stay on topic in a conversation about a non-preferred topic. Note frequency of distractions and how well the client was able to return their focus when prompted.
   - **Memory:** Memory refers to recall of both recent and remote events. It can also mean working memory, or the ability to hold and manipulate information in your mind. Working memory can be assessed by

asking the client to remember a group of words and then prompting them to recall them later in the session. Recent memory can include asking questions about what the client did prior to the session or up to a few days ago. Remote memory can mean asking about a birthday party or trip that took place months to years ago. In order to determine how accurate the client's memory is, you can get collaborative data from a parent or guardian (however, if the parent's memory is impaired, they might not be able to provide accurate information about this). Document the specifics of what the client was able to remember as well as how accurate that was.

- **Telehealth considerations:** A client's attention might shift more if they are in their home environment with more distractions. Although you can encourage guardians to give the client a space with few distractions for their appointment, this might not be an option for every family. Always consider the context.

6. **Affect and mood:** Assessing the client's mood and affect will inform many of the considerations discussed in other sections. An anxious client will speak and behave differently than a very calm client, and an excited client might be more hyperactive than a calm client. How does the client feel about being in the room with you, and in what ways are they expressing these feelings? Note any additional information on what variables outside of the session might be impacting the client's mood. For example, clients sometimes enter my office in an angry, irritable, or even hostile manner because they have just come from being disciplined at school, or they might have gotten the message that they are meeting with me because they are in trouble.
7. **Perception and reality testing:** As with the client's orientation, it is important to know what information the client has been given by their guardians prior to the appointment. Also remember the child's developmental stage; for example, it is not concerning if a very young child has an imaginary friend.
   - **Additional considerations:** Be mindful of the client's culture, family, background, and beliefs when assessing this. For example, some cultures believe that deceased relatives stay around to watch over them, whereas for others, this belief could be a sign of mental distress. Similarly, a Black client in a predominantly white school reporting that teachers or staff seem to be singling them out is likely to be experiencing racism rather than delusions of persecution.
8. **Behavior:** Describe the client's specific behaviors in the session. This includes what the client does unprompted and what they do in response to questions, interventions, or other things presented in the session. What concerns, if any, arise from these behaviors? If this is a therapy client whom you have seen several times, what changes in behavior do you observe compared to their last session or several sessions ago?
9. **Reasoning/Cognitive functioning:** How is the client's overall functioning, and (if you have seen them more than once) do they demonstrate a shift in functioning since their last appointment? Remember that "functioning" is complicated, and a client can be doing very well in one area but be struggling in another.

It can help in ensuring that language is neutral and nonbiased to indicate from where you drew each conclusion. Instead of simply noting, "The client's mood was anxious," write, "The client appeared anxious, as evidenced/indicated by (fidgeting behavior/tense posture/looking down for much of the appointment)." Justify why you drew the conclusion that they were anxious as opposed to hyperactive, neurodivergent, et cetera.

"Not Assessed"

Not every mental status examination will include every category listed here. For example, if a client does not speak in their session (whether this is because they are nonverbal, anxious, or do not want to talk to you), you would not be able to include an in-depth assessment of their speech.

If a client is in crisis, you might skip parts of the mental status examination in order to focus on addressing the crisis and ensuring their immediate safety.

It is better to indicate that a section was "not assessed" than to extrapolate from incomplete information, as this prevents you from guessing incorrectly or imposing your own biases onto the client's mental status. If you include incomplete information, it is important to indicate this and note any limitations of your conclusions based on missing knowledge.

When noting possible reasons for a behavior or mental state, it is important to indicate what is your clinical judgment rather than the observation itself. For example, if a client changes the subject frequently, you might note that they could be highly distractible or that they may not want to discuss a certain topic. However, be sure to note if the client did not explicitly indicate or give a reason for the behavior.

Language Matters!

When writing the mental status examination, think about the words you are using and what they mean in the client's record. Are you assigning value to a behavior? Why might the client be acting this way? Is your emphasis on the client's needs, or are your own feelings about their behavior impacting your clinical judgment? The purpose of the mental status examination is to provide objective data about the client's mental state rather than personal judgments, and as such, some terms ought to be avoided.

Some terms are generally problematic and not best practice or should only be used with an explanation of what you mean. Words to avoid include:

1. *Non-compliant.* It can be frustrating when a client does not do what we feel they ought to in order to feel better or make progress in treatment. However, this term suggests that the client is consciously and deliberately choosing not to do as we ask. Instead of labeling the client "non-compliant," we must take an approach of curiosity to figure out *why* they are not doing what we want them to do. When we approach with curiosity rather than judgment, we can determine the why and enable the client to better follow through in the future.
   - Is the intervention not a good fit for their personality, preferences, or needs?
     - *Instead of "non-compliant," note that the client asked to change the intervention or activity and how you adapted it to their needs.*
   - Is there a barrier to following through, such as access to care, finances, or something else?
     - *Instead of "non-compliant," document the barrier and note that the client was "unable" to comply rather than suggesting unwillingness.*
   - Did the client misunderstand what you were asking of them?
     - *Instead of "non-compliant," document what was misunderstood.*
2. *Refused.* Again, what is the reason for refusal? Anxiety, misunderstanding, confusion, or inaccessibility? Address the *why* behind the refusal.
   - *Instead of "refused," note that the client "was hesitant to ______." Document how you inquired about the hesitation and how you addressed it or modified the intervention to meet the client's need. If the client still does not feel this intervention is a good fit or something they are able to do, you can note that they "declined," as this term implies client preference rather than judgment.*
3. *Avoidant.* This term might be used in a mental status examination with appropriate context. For instance, it is acceptable to note that a client avoided discussing something that was upsetting for them. You must be mindful of what they are avoiding and why. The word *avoidant* is not necessarily something to remove

all together, but when you use this term, consider the context, the reason for the avoidance, and what that behavior looks like specifically.

- *Instead of "avoidant" (or along with "avoidant"), note the client's emotional state; if they are angry, sad, or nervous, document that.*

4. *Difficult.* There is an uncredited quote that circles the teacher and parenting blogs: "They're not *giving you* a hard time; they're *having* a hard time." Children with behavioral problems can be challenging, and clinicians can feel frustrated, but we have an obligation to be aware of our emotions and not allow them to cloud our clinical judgment. In addition, referring to a client as "difficult" is not helpful or descriptive. What behaviors are they exhibiting? What is "difficult" about their presentation? What are they struggling with?

   - *It is not good practice to label clients as "difficult." Again, note the emotion and specific behaviors the client is exhibiting. For example, "Client had an angry expression on their face and stated, 'I don't want to be here.' Client sat with back turned to the therapist and made grunting noises in response to questions rather than speaking. Therapist offered Interventions X, Y, and Z, and client declined."*

5. *Manipulative.* This term holds a lot of judgment and might make us want to push back and engage in a power struggle with the client rather than meeting them where they are. Children mirror their environments, and their behavior reflects what they are taught. In addition, children seek to get their needs and wants met. Rather than seeing a behavior as manipulative, attempt to figure out what the child is seeking with the behavior.

What Kinds of Questions Can You Ask?

As with all components of child therapy, the questions used in a mental status examination should be informed by the individual client's developmental level and needs. A mental status examination with a child might not consist of many questions; rather, you may note different components of the evaluation through interactions and play.

For areas that require more specific questions, be mindful of the client's age and life experience. Many questions presented for adults, such as "What is something you recently saw on the news?" might not work for young children. Instead, you can ask about something related to the child's individual interests (this information can be gathered from parents or guardians before you meet with the child, and a quick internet search can give you enough information to start a conversation with the child about the topic). Ask the child questions about their life (again, with information gathered from the parent or guardian prior to the session) to assess for perception, cognition, and thought content. For working memory tasks, consider giving the child a list of words related to their topic of interest to recall later in the session rather than numbers.

Puzzles or logic tasks to ascertain cognition might need to be simplified and made age-appropriate. You can purchase various puzzles to keep on hand and present an age-appropriate option to the child. Always bring your conclusions back to the child's age, development, life experience, and any specific cultural considerations.

Samples

This chapter includes three sample mental status examinations, with a blank template of each provided for easy reproduction. The three templates are fill-in-the-blank forms with prompts for each section, a more specific form with check boxes, and an open-ended form using more narrative paragraphs.

You might find that one form best fits your writing style. In my practice, I find that the narrative helps me think through my client's presentation best, but others might prefer more specific prompts to ensure they do not miss an important category. Although payers can accept narrative notes, you must ensure that your narrative includes all necessary components. You may also decide to use one form for certain types of clients. The check boxes and fill-in-the-blank forms can be helpful if you accept insurance, as it ensures that various categories are addressed that the payer might require.

Although best practices exist for a reason, there is room for your unique style. These forms aim to help make your documentation efficient, thorough, and comprehensive.

CASE EXAMPLE #1

A seven-year-old male presents with possible anxiety. In the office, he curls up on the couch, puts his head on his knees, and does not speak. He appears tense and sits with a rigid posture and does not move for several minutes. Over time, you are able to coax him to play a game of Uno with you, and he uses nods and head shakes to answer yes and no questions about the game. In play, he closely follows the rules of the game, with the exception of holding up one finger rather than saying, "Uno." He is nonverbal for the entire session but plays the game with you, looking at you occasionally and smiling when he wins.

Sample Mental Status Examination: Fill-in-the-Blank

Client Name: [Redacted]

Client Date of Birth: [Redacted]

Presenting Problem: Anxiety symptoms

Appearance: Client presented in clean, weather-appropriate clothing.

Hygiene: Client appeared appropriately groomed, with good hygiene.

Eye Contact: At the start of the appointment, client did not make eye contact. As he became more comfortable, he made some eye contact while playing the game.

Orientation: Client appeared to be oriented to place; however, further information about orientation could not be assessed due to the client not speaking in session.

Speech: Client did not speak in the session, possibly due to discomfort or nervousness.

Attention/Focus: When client engaged in the Uno game, he was able to focus and remained engaged in the activity.

Memory: Not assessed due to client not speaking in session.

Affect and Mood: Client appeared rigid and shut down at the start of the appointment, suggesting anxiety about the appointment. He became more relaxed, engaged, and happier over time.

Perception and Reality Testing: Not assessed due to client not speaking in the session.

Behavior: Client came into the session and curled up on the couch with his head down. He did not engage initially but appeared more comfortable over time. He was able to engage in the Uno game but remained nonverbal for the duration of the appointment. In the game, he took turns and followed the rules of the activity.

Cognitive Functioning: Client was able to follow instructions in the activity presented. Further assessment of cognitive functioning could not be conducted due to client not being able to engage verbally.

Other Information: ______________________________

Sample Mental Status Examination: Fill-in-the-Blank

Client Name: ____________________

Client Date of Birth: ____________________

Presenting Problem: ____________________

Appearance: ____________________

____

Hygiene: ____________________

____

Eye Contact: ____________________

____

Orientation: ____________________

____

____

Speech: ____________________

____

Attention/Focus: ____________________

____

Memory: ____________________

____

Affect and Mood: ____________________

____

____

Perception and Reality Testing: ____________________

____

____

Behavior: ____________________

____

____

Cognitive Functioning: ____________________

____

____

Other Information: ____________________

____

____

CASE EXAMPLE #2

A sixteen-year-old female presents as very animated. She bounces as she sits and taps her feet. She speaks continuously throughout the appointment, switches topics frequently, and gestures frequently with her hands. Topics include schoolwork, interactions with friends, and her family. The information she shares is not unrealistic, but many details contradict information provided by her parents prior to the session. For example, the parents stated that she chooses to play video games rather than finishing homework, but the client stated that she feels unable to start assignments due to feeling high pressure and not knowing where to start big tasks. She also stated that her parents "yell at me" about her academic difficulties, and the parents reported having "discussions" where they "express concern" about her.

Sample Mental Status Examination: Check Boxes

Client Name: [Redacted]

Client Date of Birth: [Redacted]

Appearance: ☒ Appropriate ☐ Disheveled ☐ Eccentric ☐ Other: ________

Hygiene: ☒ Appropriate ☐ Other: ________

Eye Contact: ☐ Typical ☐ Avoidant ☒ Intense ☐ Other: ________

Orientation: ☒ x3: Person, place, and time ☐ Not oriented to person ☐ Not oriented to place ☐ Not oriented to time ☐ Other: ________

Speech: ☐ Typical ☐ Pressured ☒ Rapid ☐ Slow ☐ Slurred ☐ Other: ________

Attention/Focus: ☐ Typical ☒ Distractible ☐ Fixations/Obsessions ☐ Other: ________

Memory: ☐ Typical ☐ Poor remote memory ☐ Poor recent memory ☐ Poor working memory ☒ Other: Client's report of history contradicts parent's report.

Affect: ☐ Congruent ☐ Incongruent ☐ Blunted ☐ Labile ☐ Tearful ☐ Flat ☐ Constricted ☒ Animated ☐ Reactive ☐ Other: ________

Mood: ☐ Euthymic ☐ Irritable ☒ Elevated/Manic ☐ Depressed ☐ Anxious ☐ Calm ☒ Other: ________

Perception and Reality Testing: ☐ Typical ☐ Logical ☐ Disorganized

☐ Other: Not assessed due to inconsistencies in history; more information is needed.

☐ Hallucinations: ________ ☐ Delusions: ________

Behavior: ☐ Typical movement ☐ Unusual movement ☐ Typical activity ☒ Atypical activity

Cognitive Functioning: ☐ Good insight ☐ Good judgment ☐ Insight deficit ☐ Judgment deficit

☒ Other: Not assessed; more information needed about inconsistencies.

Other Information: Rapid movement and gestures

____

Sample Mental Status Examination: Check Boxes

Client Name: ______________________________

Client Date of Birth: ______________________________

Appearance: ☐ Appropriate ☐ Disheveled ☐ Eccentric ☐ Other: ____________

Hygiene: ☐ Appropriate ☐ Other: ______________________________

Eye Contact: ☐ Typical ☐ Avoidant ☐ Intense ☐ Other: ____________

Orientation: ☐ x3: Person, place, and time ☐ Not oriented to person ☐ Not oriented to place
☐ Not oriented to time ☐ Other: ______________________________

Speech: ☐ Typical ☐ Pressured ☐ Rapid ☐ Slow ☐ Slurred ☐ Other: ____________

Attention/Focus: ☐ Typical ☐ Distractible ☐ Fixations/Obsessions ☐ Other: ____________

Memory: ☐ Typical ☐ Poor remote memory ☐ Poor recent memory ☐ Poor working memory
☐ Other: Client's report of history contradicts parent's report.

Affect: ☐ Congruent ☐ Incongruent ☐ Blunted ☐ Labile ☐ Tearful ☐ Flat ☐ Constricted
☐ Animated ☐ Reactive ☐ Other: ______________________________

Mood: ☐ Euthymic ☐ Irritable ☐ Elevated/Manic ☐ Depressed ☐ Anxious ☐ Calm
☐ Other: ______________________________

Perception and Reality Testing: ☐ Typical ☐ Logical ☐ Disorganized ☐ Other: ____________
☐ Hallucinations: ____________________ ☐ Delusions: ____________________

Behavior: ☐ Typical movement ☐ Unusual movement ☐ Typical activity ☐ Atypical activity

Cognitive Functioning: ☐ Good insight ☐ Good judgment ☐ Insight deficit ☐ Judgment deficit
☐ Other: ______________________________

Other Information: ______________________________

____

____

____

____

____

CASE EXAMPLE #3

A twelve-year-old female asks to "just talk" in her session. She stands up very straight and walks back to the office, where she sits with straight posture in a chair. She answers all questions and has a wide vocabulary, often using many-syllable words. She appears compliant and friendly, and she talks like someone much older. She appears to be in good spirits, though when asked about unpleasant feelings, she has trouble thinking of examples. She can describe sadness as an abstract concept but stated that she cannot think of a time that she has felt this way.

Sample Mental Status Examination: Paragraph Format

Client presented for the appointment in neat, appropriate clothing with good hygiene. She appeared calm and was compliant and friendly. She declined to engage in a game with the therapist and chose to converse instead. Her speech had typical rate and volume, with extensive vocabulary, and her mood was overall positive. She spoke about positive things in her life, including [examples], but struggled to come up with examples for unpleasant feelings. No hallucinations, delusions, or disorganized thinking were noted, and her memory and concentration seemed typical. She was oriented to person, place, and time, and no issues with judgment were noted in the appointment.

Glossary of Terms

affect: The emotion that a person expresses in a given moment.

appearance: Information pertaining to how the client appears: Their clothing, grooming, hygiene, et cetera.

attention: The client's ability to direct their mind toward specific thoughts or behaviors.

avoidant: Pulling away from something, often due to discomfort.

Brief Mental Status Examination (BMSE): A short mental status examination, often used for progress notes to provide current information about the client's symptoms and presentation that day.

clinical judgment: The provider's use of their expertise to draw conclusions about the client's behavior, statements, and presentation.

cognitive functioning: An individual's ability to perform thought-based tasks, such as solving puzzles or using logical reasoning.

crisis: When symptoms escalate suddenly, and the client experiences acute psychological distress, often requiring immediate intervention.

developmental range: The variety of milestones that a child reaches within a time frame.

developmentally appropriate: When cognition, skills, or abilities are within the typical and expected developmental range.

developmentally typical: When cognition, skills, or abilities are within normal limits based on the child's age.

diagnostic impression: The DSM or ICD codes for which the provider has determined the client meets criteria.

difficult: When the provider is struggling to connect with the client; this term implies that the client is deliberately challenging or resisting the provider.

eye contact: The extent to which the client looks the provider in the eyes; what is appropriate varies by age, setting, and cultural background.

focus: Concentrating one's attention on a specific topic or activity.

functioning: The client's ability to care for themselves, understand the world around them, and achieve their personal goals.

hygiene: The client's cleanliness and grooming.

manipulative: Deliberately attempting to control a situation by playing to someone's emotions rather than asking directly.

mental capacity: The ability to make appropriate, healthy decisions for oneself.

Mental Status Examination (MSE): Detailed information about a client's current capacity and functioning, including observations about appearance, emotion, and behavior.

mood: Emotional state; more sustained and long-term than affect.

non-compliant: When a client does not comply with what the provider wants them to do; this term assumes that the client is making a conscious choice to refuse to do what the provider wants.

not assessed: A term used when the provider did not evaluate a section of the mental status examination.

orientation: A client's ability to understand their situation with regard to where they are, who they are, and when they are.

perception: A client's ability to identify and interpret sensory information.

reality testing: A client's ability to determine what of their perception is accurate and correctly interpret stimuli in the world around them.

recent memory: A client's memory of things that occurred recently.
refused: When a client declines to do what a provider has asked; this term implies defiance on the client's part.
regression: When symptoms that had improved worsen again, or when skills that were previously mastered become more difficult for the client again.
remote memory: Recall of events that occurred long ago.
speech: The client's verbal language in the session, including speed of talking, tone of voice, and any unusual use of specific words or phrases.

Works Cited

Centers for Disease Control and Prevention. (2022, February 15). *Learn about child development.* Centers for Disease Control and Prevention. Retrieved September 21, 2022, from www.cdc.gov/ncbddd/childdevelopment/index.html

FitzGerald, C., & Hurst, S. (2017). Implicit bias in healthcare professionals: A systematic review. *BMC Medical Ethics, 18*(1), 1–18.

Kazdin, A. E. (2003). Psychotherapy for children and adolescents. *Annual Review of Psychology, 54,* 253.

Norris, D. R., Clark, M. S., & Shipley, S. (2016). The mental status examination. *American Family Physician, 94*(8), 635–641.

CHAPTER 8

PROGRESS NOTES

Other than actual sessions, progress notes probably take up the biggest chunk of time from a therapist's day. You have seen all your clients for the day, but you aren't done yet! First you must document each session in a progress note. There are legal and ethical requirements that go into a thorough progress note, but you must also consider your client's privacy – for children and teens in particular, a parent or guardian may gain access to their notes. You must ensure that your notes meet all necessary standards while protecting your client.

What Are Progress Notes?

Progress notes are an important part of each client's medical record. Every time a client has an appointment, their provider creates a progress note detailing their treatment and what occurred during that session. It includes information about what happened in the appointment, what interventions were used, how the client responded to those interventions, the client's current symptoms, and documentation of the medical necessity of treatment. Therapists also note information about changes in symptoms, updates to the treatment plan, and additional relevant information (Boyles, 2022a).

All ethical codes include instructions about the importance of progress notes and documentation for each session, and there are legal requirements therapists must follow in completing progress notes. In addition, if a therapist accepts insurance, the payer may require certain information or standards for progress notes (Lees et al., 2015). More information about insurance requirements for documentation is detailed in Chapter 3.

What About Process Notes?

Unlike progress notes, process notes are not a required component of a client's treatment. Technically, a process note is any documentation that is not part of a formal note that the therapist creates for the session (Boyles, 2022a).

For example, if I keep a notepad and pen handy during a session and jot down some thoughts during the session, that piece of paper is not necessarily entered into the chart as official documentation but instead is a reference point for me later when keeping my notes. I have done this to ensure that I remember an important detail that the client mentioned so that I do not forget to include it in the official note. What I noted during the session is a process note, and I destroy it after the information is transferred into the progress note, since all information in the process note is now part of an official progress note.

DOI: 10.4324/9781003316442-8

You might compare process notes to a syringe that is used to draw blood for medical testing. While the syringe was used in the client's treatment, it is not a part of that client's medical record. If releasing the client's records, a doctor would not include the syringe but just the results of the actual tests run on the blood.

A process note is sometimes more formal as well. It may include questions a therapist wants to bring to supervision or consultation, considerations about differential diagnoses the therapist wants to research further before formally adding them to the chart, or information that the therapist wants to remember but does not want to add to the official chart. (Reasons why a therapist might want to keep information out of the official chart will be discussed later in this chapter.)

Some documentation generated from the session itself may also be a process note. This depends on the nature of the intervention and its relevance to the client's treatment overall. For example, a worksheet to help a client identify which coping skills they find most effective might be attached to a progress note for reference in the future.

However, a trauma narrative generated as part of a Trauma-Focused Cognitive Behavioral Therapy (TF-CBT) protocol might be kept as a process note to preserve the client's confidentiality. Some children who are referred for TF-CBT are also part of ongoing court proceedings; for instance, if their perpetrator is on trial for abusing the child. A prosecutor may subpoena the child's therapy records for use in court, and a judge may deem this release necessary for the trial. In this case, the therapist will have no choice but to share the child's records with the court, meaning that the perpetrator will likely gain access to the child's progress notes.

Obviously, a client could be harmed if their perpetrator reads their trauma narrative without their consent. Many would not agree to have their perpetrator see their trauma narrative. Additionally, trauma narratives emphasize the client's experience of the trauma and their emotional reaction rather than accurate facts (Arkansas Building Effective Services for Trauma, 2016). They are not forensic documents and cannot be relied upon as having completely factual information about the crime itself. As such, a provider may not include the full trauma narrative as a part of the client's official progress notes.

Since process notes are not officially part of the client's medical record, they are not typically included in chart requests (Landau & Reamer, 2022). For example, if a client requests that their chart be released to their physician, lawyer, or another provider, process notes are not included in the standard chart. However, a lawyer can still request that a judge order process notes to be released, so even though they have added protection of not being part of the "official" medical record, therapists must still be mindful of this possibility when documenting information in process notes. A judge is more likely to uphold the privacy of process notes since they have more specific protections when it comes to court proceedings, but this is not a guarantee (Lees et al., 2015).

If you are ordered by a judge to release process notes, contact the judge directly and explain your concerns regarding harm to your client if their process notes are released. Let them know also if the process notes are unlikely to be helpful in the court proceeding. This may convince the judge to preserve your client's well-being and privacy by not ordering the release, or they may agree to let you release process records *only* to the judge so that no one else involved in the case will gain access to the information.

Documentation about mandated reporting may also be kept as a process note if, for instance, the legal guardian has access to progress notes but is the alleged perpetrator. The therapist may keep information about allegations out of the official progress notes and chart to protect the child's privacy. In this case, though, that documentation would be an official part of the record for the purposes of legal proceedings.

Concurrent Notes

Many therapists complete notes after the session has ended and the client has left the office. However, depending on your therapeutic approach and style, practice requirements, or jurisdictional requirements, you may choose to complete notes concurrently with your client or during the session itself. Take the client's age and developmental level into consideration when making this decision. For instance, a four-year-old attending play therapy may not understand the purpose of a progress note and may not be able to provide feedback. An older child or teen might have input on what was important to their session.

If you are aware that a client's parent, guardian, caseworker, or other involved party is going to get access to their notes, it can be good for the therapeutic relationship (and ethical) to complete your notes with the client present. That way, the client is aware of exactly what information you are sharing through the progress note.

Concurrent notes can also help you and the client process how treatment is going. A teen who states that they want to work through a traumatic event but then focuses on other concerns during the session may be able to sit with and address their hesitancy about their readiness for that part of the process if it is brought to their attention in this process.

Components of a Progress Note

While progress notes can be formatted several different ways, certain information must be included. The amount of detail in various sections may depend on your specific jurisdictional and ethical requirements, and the specific case. The following sections are included in a progress note:

1. **Who was present and when:** If you meet with your client individually for the full session, this section is very simple to complete, as you simply note that only the client was present. However, often therapy with children and adolescents includes parent or guardian involvement. If you had a parent or guardian check in at the start or end of the session for 10 minutes, you need to note, for example, "Client's mother met with the therapist individually for the first 10 minutes of the appointment. Client then met with the therapist individually for the remaining 35 minutes of the appointment." It is important to note the parent or guardian's presence, whether you saw them with the client present or without, and how much of the session time this took up. A parent may have a concern that you feel is best discussed with the parent alone, which you would note and justify in your documentation. For example, if I have feedback for a parent about their parenting choices, I address this without the client present so that I do not undermine the parent's role as an authority figure in front of the child. This is often necessary and appropriate when you are a therapist who works with children, and my documentation should reflect what I chose as well as my clinical justification for the choice.
2. **Location of the session:** As was discussed in Chapter 4, note where the session took place (usually your office unless the client was seen via telehealth). As with intake sessions, telehealth sessions should note the following:
   a. **Safety/Privacy:** Note that you checked in and confirmed the client's location at the time of the session, as well as checking to be sure that the client was in a physically safe location and felt they had privacy.
   b. **Security/Encryption:** Note that you used a HIPAA-compliant platform to conduct the session or a system that is compliant with applicable jurisdiction.
   c. **Justification:** Note why the session was conducted via telehealth.

d. **Sample telehealth note:** You can, of course, tailor the wording based on what was appropriate. Sample telehealth documentation may include: "This session was conducted via secure, encrypted, HIPAA-compliant videoconferencing utilizing a Zoom meeting. The session was conducted via telehealth due to [Note the justification here]. The therapist confirmed the client's location at the start of session [Note the specific location, if different from the address listed in the client's chart]. The client confirmed they were in a safe, private location at the time of service." Sample justifications may include the following:

   i. "The client's physical illness/disability puts them at high risk for complications should they contract a viral infection, and the client is safer completing sessions from home, where they are not exposed to potential contamination in the waiting room or office."

   ii. "The client's physical location is a 90-minute drive from the therapist's office, and they are unable to commute a total of three hours for a therapy appointment. As such, telehealth is utilized to increase accessibility for services."

   iii. "The client does not have access to reliable transportation and is seen from home to increase accessibility for services."

   iv. "Due to scheduling difficulties, the client was unable to present for an in-person session but was able to join from [Location], as they did not have to commute to the session."

3. **Billing code, if applicable:** Specific billing codes are detailed in Chapter 3. Each progress note must include the proper session billing code, and the code must be appropriate for insurance billing if the client is using insurance to cover the session.

4. **Session content:** Essentially, this refers to what occurred in the session. What were the topics discussed, and how did the client behave? What did the client bring up in the session, and what topics did the therapist bring up? This is typically presented as a brief narrative of the session.

5. **Interventions used:** Details about what interventions a therapist used in the session can be listed separately or woven into the session content section. This information is important both to the treatment plan and for payers. Therapists should note what therapeutic interventions occurred in session or were given to the client to practice in between sessions. They can also include justification for these interventions, including why they are appropriate for the client, how they are clinically indicated based on the client's presenting symptoms and diagnosis, and information about their effectiveness based on available research and evidence.

6. **Comments on the treatment plan:** Tie the session content and interventions into the client's treatment plan (discussed in Chapter 6). This includes justification for the session content and interventions based on the client's pre-established goals. In addition, the therapist will note how the client is progressing regarding their treatment goals. For example, if a client wants to develop appropriate skills for managing their anxiety symptoms and reduce the severity of their anxiety, have they experienced more or less anxiety since treatment started? What skills have they worked on, and have these skills been effective? Is there a need to adjust the treatment plan based on new goals or events in the client's life?

7. **Diagnostic updates:** A client's diagnosis often stays the same for much of their treatment. However, it is possible that the client will bring up new symptoms in their session. A therapist will not necessarily change the client's diagnosis every time a new symptom is mentioned, but they may note an increase of certain symptoms or that new symptoms have emerged. For example, a client who presents for treatment of depression may have a diagnosis of Major Depressive Disorder (MDD). If the client begins reporting periods of excessive energy, reduced need for sleep, and feelings of grandiosity, a therapist might note in their diagnosis that the client is showing some symptoms that could indicate mania or hypomania. They may monitor these symptoms over time before determining whether an update from MDD to a bipolar-type disorder is appropriate. Depending on the therapist's credentials, they may need to refer the client to an appropriate diagnostician instead of changing the diagnosis themselves. However, if the therapist is

qualified to make a new diagnosis, they may change the client's diagnosis once they have determined that the existing diagnosis is inaccurate or no longer reflects the client's presenting symptoms.

8. **Plan:** This refers to what the client and therapist (and client's guardian, when appropriate) have decided are the next steps. This includes when the next session will occur, any "homework" given by the therapist for the client to practice in between sessions, and any referrals the therapist is making.
9. **Safety concerns:** This will be covered in more detail in Chapter 10 of this text. Safety concerns include any risk assessment completed in the session and notes of any concerns about suicide, self-harm, harm to others, mandatory reporting issues, or other safety issues that came up in the session. If a safety concern emerged in a previous section, this should include any updated information about the concern and any changes in the treatment plan or next steps based on the client's current level of risk.

There are many different templates and starting points that a therapist can use when creating their progress notes. The different options have various benefits and drawbacks. As with all aspects of clinical documentation, as long as the legal and ethical requirements are met, clinicians can decide for themselves which template best fits their style and documentation needs.

SOAP Notes

SOAP Notes include objective and factual information about sessions, and some insurances prefer this approach due to its emphasis on verifiable information. They are broken down into four components that cover the necessary information for a progress note (Podder et al., 2021):

1. **Subjective:** This section includes information provided by the client about their presenting concerns and current symptoms, updates about their situation or life events, and any changes to their goals or needs. It may include direct quotes from the client about their experience.
2. **Objective:** This includes only information that is specific and factual, such as mental status examination, appearance, and behavior in the session. Note whether this is in contrast or consistent with their presentation in previous sessions. Treatment interventions used in the session are also noted here.
3. **Assessment:** This is the therapist's clinical impression of the client's symptoms based on information provided in the first two sections. This includes information about regression or progress in treatment as well as any changes in diagnosis.
4. **Plan:** Finally, note intentions for the future, including when the next session will be, what the client might work on in the meantime, any appropriate referrals, and anything the therapist is putting together for an intervention in the next appointment.

BIRP Notes

Although similar to SOAP notes, BIRP notes focus less on specific, quantifiable aspects of the session and more on the overall tone or feeling of the session. BIRP notes are also broken down into four sections to describe what occurred in the session (Boyles, 2022b):

1. **Behavior:** This includes both your observations and the client's self-report. This means their behavior in the session as well as what has been happening outside of the session. You can speak to specific symptoms as well as behaviors in general.
2. **Intervention:** As the name suggests, this section includes the specific interventions used in the session, including those indicated in the treatment plan and any that were used based on what came up in the

moment. If an intervention deviates from the treatment plan, you should also note the clinical justification. For example, if a safety issue arose in a session, you might implement a risk assessment and develop a safety plan and note that this was necessary even though it was not part of the client's initial reason for seeking treatment.

3. **Response:** How did the client respond to the interventions used in session? You are specifically seeking feedback from the client about what worked and what did not work for them, as well as your observations that speak to their response. (For example, sometimes trauma survivors struggle with people pleasing and might be hesitant to say outright that they are uncomfortable with an intervention. Note whether you observed this and how you addressed it with the client.) This section should also include how you handled the client's response to an intervention. If the client found an intervention unhelpful, how did you adjust and respond to this feedback? What did you change in order to ensure their needs were met?
4. **Plan:** This is the same as the Plan section of SOAP notes: Indicate the next session, things for the client to work on in between appointments, referrals made, and things for the therapist to bring to the next session.

PIRP Notes

PIRP notes are similar to BIRP notes in that they include Intervention, Response, and Plan sections. However, the first section differs, with emphasis on Problem rather than Behavior. The problem section focuses on a specific issue the client is facing, which may be a symptom, life stressor, or other concern rather than specific behaviors the client is exhibiting.

GIRP Notes

GIRP notes also include Intervention, Response, and Plan sections with the same format and information as PIRP and BIRP notes. With GIRP notes, the note format starts with the Goal of the session. Essentially, what do the client and therapist hope to gain from the session or from treatment as a whole?

BIRP Versus PIRP Versus GIRP Notes

Since these three note formats have overlap, you can easily change your template to reflect which note type is most appropriate for a given session. Sometimes, clients come with a specific goal in mind, or they have a problem they want to explore. You might also have a note that needs to address behaviors *and* the client's goal, so you may want to add a fifth section and make a BGIRP note in that case. The following can indicate when each note format is the best fit (Boyles, 2022c):

1. **BIRP:** Since this note emphasizes the client's presenting behavior and their report of behavioral changes, this format can help the therapist better understand the client as a whole and see how they function in their life outside of the session.
2. **PIRP:** This format is most appropriate when a session focuses on solving, addressing, or working through a specific, identified problem or issue that the client is experiencing.
3. **GIRP:** GIRP notes aim to help a client reach a goal they have articulated. The difference here is that instead of working through an existing problem, the client is working toward a goal. Think of PIRP notes as trying to bring the client up to baseline and GIRP notes as trying to progress the client beyond their pre-existing baseline toward greater progress in their life.

It is likely that the same client will fit into each of these categories in different sessions or at different points in their treatment. All three emphases have their place in treatment, and having all available to you can help you be flexible based on your client's needs on a given day. There will likely be sessions where a combination note is appropriate, where the therapist feels it is important to note behaviors, goals, and problems presented by the client.

Documenting Play

Therapists who work with young children face specific challenges in documenting their sessions, especially in sessions that involve play therapy. When a child client guides their session and the session consists primarily of games and imaginative play activities, this must then be written in a progress note in a way that meets legal, ethical, and payer standards. Since play therapy is generally considered a standard in the field, it is possible to justify these interventions and document play therapy appropriately (Cassado-Frankel, 2016). In Chapter 6, we detailed the evidence base behind play therapy with children and its appropriateness in a child's treatment plan. So what does this look like in progress note documentation?

First, include your therapeutic approach in the session. Note whether the session was non-directive, client-centered, cognitive behavioral, narrative, or something else. Next, indicate the facts of what occurred in the session. If the session primarily consisted of play with a doll house, state this. You can state that you created space for the client to process emotions in a developmentally appropriate manner through play.

Document the child's emotional state and how this changed through the session, including specifically what was occurring in play when this happened and the child's emotional response. Note any themes that seemed to come up repeatedly in play. Also note your role in the play session and the child's interaction or engagement with you. If you primarily observed and narrated as the child engaged in play, you can indicate this and say that you pointed out emotions as the client demonstrated them to improve self-awareness and insight.

If the session included any skill practice or building as a component of play, indicate this as well. Tie these skills into the treatment plan and goals created at the start of therapy. Finally, indicate how the themes that came up in play relate to the client's presenting concerns and treatment goals.

Confidentiality and Progress Notes

Therapy notes are considered confidential under HIPAA, but minor clients experience specific limitations to their confidentiality because they are underage. When writing progress notes, therapists must be aware of potential limitations of this confidentiality and take steps to protect our clients.

As always, we must first always be aware of the laws relevant in the jurisdiction or jurisdictions in which we are practicing. In some states, minors gain the right to confidentiality over their medical records before they turn 18. If, for instance, you practice in a state where medical confidentiality begins at age 16, you actually need your client's written consent to share any details about their care with the legal guardian unless the guardian has a court order stating otherwise. In addition, some states have flexibility that a therapist can use their clinical judgment to withhold information from a parent in certain circumstances (for example, therapists are permitted to withhold information about a mandated report if they believe divulging this information to the guardian would lead to harm to the client).

Outside of these circumstances, we must be aware that a guardian could potentially gain access to a child or teen's therapy progress notes. In addition, they may choose to release these notes to the child's school or other organization. We can discourage this and explain the risks, but we may be legally obligated to comply with a request for records. Additionally, we can be up front about boundaries around releasing records when we start therapy (as discussed in Chapter 6), but a parent or guardian may change their mind later and request records even though they previously said they would not. Again, depending on the laws where you practice, you may be obligated to comply.

As such, when you write progress notes for children and teens, you do so with the assumption that the parent or guardian may one day see the notes. You must consider the possible impact on your client if this occurs.

While progress notes need to include accurate information about what occurred in the session, there is some leeway with how much specific detail is included. For example, a client might express that they are exploring their sexual orientation or gender identity, and they are worried that their parents would kick them out or abuse them if the parents learned that the child was exploring this. In this case, a therapist may choose to indicate that the client worked on exploring their identity in the session without specifically mentioning sexual orientation and gender.

Privacy concerns related to progress notes are not always related to an immediate safety issue. A client might disclose a disagreement that they had with a friend at school and ask the therapist not to share the argument with the parent, or they may share that they participate in an activity because the parent likes it and are trying to figure out how to tell the parent that they want to quit. In both of these cases, if the parent sees this information in the client's record, the client could lose trust in the therapist and experience a rupture in the therapeutic relationship. This is still harmful to the client even though it does not create risk to the client's physical or emotional safety.

When a child experiences a trust rupture with a therapist, they might not ever be able to build trust back again, depending on the nature of the rupture. This could also interfere with the client's ability to build trust with future providers even if they start seeing a different therapist in the future. They may feel that you were unable to keep their confidence, and therefore all therapists are untrustworthy. We have a duty to maintain trust and privacy with clients as much as possible, outside of mandated reporting issues.

Progress notes can detail that a client discussed their identity, relationships, conflicts, coping skills, or emotions without divulging specific information that the client requested be kept confidential. Interventions used in the session can be listed without including this information as well. You may consider doing concurrent notes so that the client sees what is input in the record and understands what the parent or guardian might see if they request access to the chart.

Progress Notes and the Legal System

Although the confidentiality of medical records is protected under HIPAA, there are circumstances under which others may gain access to a client's chart and progress notes as part of a legal process. These situations include:

1. **Child abuse investigations:** Therapists in all United States are mandated reporters and are required to report child abuse to the appropriate regulatory body when they learn of an allegation. Depending on the results of the investigation, they may be asked to provide progress notes and treatment information as part of prosecution for child abuse.

2. **Custody battles:** If the client's parents are divorcing or have divorced, one or both parents or their attorneys may request the child's therapy records as evidence for the proceedings. It is important to note that, even if the child's therapist is trained as a custody evaluator, it is not appropriate for the primary therapist to serve in the role of custody evaluator or make a recommendation about custody for their client.

3. **Disability claims:** If the client has a documented disability, the guardian may request records as part of their application for services or support.

While there are cases where progress notes are an important part of the legal process (such as when documenting a pattern of negligence or abusive behavior during a child protection investigation), records releases always come with risk. If a child shares information in session that later becomes part of the court record, this can severely damage trust and the therapeutic relationship. In addition, if a child discloses abuse and the records are released for court, the abuser may learn that the child "told on them" and retaliate against the child. Similarly, in custody battles, a child may worry that things they said in session could be used against one or both parents. They may also fear rejection by a parent who learns what was said in session.

If there is a legal request for your records, determine the nature of the request. If you receive a subpoena from a lawyer, you must get consent from the client or their legal guardian before releasing records. In cases where the parents are divorced or separated, you must get consent from both parties before releasing information (Disla de Jesus et al., 2022). If one or both parents refuse to authorize release, you are required to let the requesting attorney know. They must then request that the judge issue a court order requiring the release of the records. Therapists are required to comply with court orders from judges (Landau & Reamer, 2022).

In addition to gaining appropriate consent to release records, you may have concerns about releasing records. As already noted, you may be concerned about the therapeutic relationship and broken trust with your client if records are released, or you may feel that your client will be harmed as a direct result of records being released. In this case, you must still respond to a subpoena or court order. Let the attorney or judge know your concerns about releasing the records, and they may be willing to change the request to protect your client. Options may include:

1. **Release of limited records:** Instead of the full chart, you may only need to release records for specific dates of service or related to certain topics.
2. **Release of sealed records:** The judge may authorize you to release the records directly to the court rather than to council so that the judge can review the records without attorneys or parents seeing them.
3. **Treatment summaries:** Instead of the full chart, you may be permitted to write a treatment summary a few pages in length detailing a review of what has been addressed in therapy, diagnosis, presenting concerns, and progress. This not only protects the client from having their entire record released but also saves the court significant time and resources. Progress notes add up over time, and a client who has been in therapy for more than a year may have hundreds of pages of notes, most of which are unlikely to be relevant.

Termination Notes

Following the end of treatment, best practice indicates that we must document that a client has discontinued services (Staff, 2019). This ensures that you have current and accurate information about your caseload and availability. This additionally ensures you have clear, specific boundaries about who is and is not a current client for purposes of record requests and liability.

Clients terminate treatment for a myriad of reasons, and the therapist is not always privy to this information, especially if a client discontinues treatment suddenly and does not choose to tell the therapist why they have stopped treatment. This is their right, though it can be helpful as a therapist to know whether there is something you could have done differently or better.

A termination note should include a reason for terminating the case, though if the reason is not given, the therapist can indicate simply that the client discontinued treatment or discontinued contact with the therapist without giving a specific reason. Other reasons for discontinuing treatment may be that the client has reached their treatment goals and no longer needs therapy, the therapist has realized they are not the best fit or trained in the client's presenting issue and made an appropriate referral, or the client has violated the terms of service (for example, ethical codes indicate that a therapist has the right to terminate treatment with a client who is threatening or stalking the therapist).

Termination notes should also include a brief overview of the client's presenting issue, their treatment plan, and what interventions were used in treatment. Note the duration of treatment, progress made, new symptoms that emerged, and regression. Note the diagnosis at intake and any changes in diagnosis over the course of treatment.

If a client is taking a planned break in treatment, you may still choose to write a termination note documenting the anticipated start and stop for the break. For instance, a child with divorced parents who live in different states might spend their summer with the other parent. If the therapist is not licensed to practice in that state, they may be unable to meet with the therapist over the summer. That therapist would write a temporary termination note indicating the plan to return to treatment in the fall.

Samples

On the next pages, you will find examples of SOAP and B/P/GIRP notes, as well as an open-ended progress note option for those who do not follow one of these specific formats. Since BIRP, PIRP, and GIRP notes have significant formatting overlap, separate formats are not provided for these. The therapist can simply substitute the first section with whatever is most appropriate. However, examples of how that first section may differ are provided in the example, with Behavior, Problem, and Goal sections all included. The example presents how the note would be written if only one format was used in the final note; however, as indicated previously, a therapist might choose to include two or three formats merged if this feels appropriate based on session goals and content.

In addition, you will find a sample treatment summary and sample termination note. Since a treatment summary is typically submitted in the form of a letter, there is not a blank template for this, but you may use the sample as a starting point in creating your own treatment summaries.

Please note that typically a progress note will include a brief mental status examination of how the client presented for a given appointment as well as information about their current diagnosis, with updates to the diagnosis as appropriate. Because these aspects of documentation are covered in other chapters of this book, they are not included in this chapter as well. In creating progress notes templates for your practice, you can attach templates for the MSE, risk assessment, diagnosis, et cetera to the progress note template.

Following the examples provided on subsequent pages, you will find a blank sample progress note with a brief MSE template and a place for risk assessment and diagnosis to be noted.

Sample SOAP Note

Client: [CLIENT] (16-year-old female)

Who Was Present: [PARENT] individually for 25 minutes; [CLIENT] with [PARENT] for 20 minutes

Session Date and Time: July 19, 2024

Subjective: [PARENT] stated that [CLIENT] was suspended from school Thursday for being intoxicated in class. [PARENT] spoke with [CLIENT] about this, and [CLIENT] disclosed drinking vodka before school with a peer about one day per week for the last month. [PARENT] stated that [CLIENT] also shared that she has been engaging in cutting behavior with a razor blade, which she gave to [PARENT] for safety. [PARENT] indicates she is unsure whether [CLIENT] needs to go to the hospital. [CLIENT] indicates that [PARENT]'s report of events is accurate. [CLIENT] indicated a desire to discontinue self-harm behavior and denies suicidal ideation.

Objective: [PARENT] expressed anxiety about client's well-being and safety. [PARENT] indicates commitment to taking whatever steps are necessary to keep [CLIENT] safe as well as to address concerns about self-harm and substance use. [CLIENT] presents as fully oriented, engaged, and compliant. [CLIENT] appears fatigued with slowed movement but is alert and denies current substance intoxication. Utilized Safety Plan intervention to ensure [PARENT] and [CLIENT] agree about whether and when hospitalization is necessary, including crisis resources. Completed risk assessment and facilitated communication between [CLIENT] and [PARENT] through family therapy.

Assessment: [CLIENT] and [PARENT] both indicate commitment to the developed safety plan. [PARENT] has possession of [CLIENT]'s razor and is keeping it locked up. [CLIENT]'s insight, compliance, and engagement suggest that they are presently Low Risk for self-harm, though this could change should a crisis arise. [CLIENT]'s depressive symptoms seem to have increased based on their behaviors, and their substance use is a new behavior that was not previously reported.

Plan: [CLIENT] and [PARENT] will follow the agreed-upon safety plan, including utilizing crisis services as appropriate and hospitalization should [CLIENT] feel she is unable to remain safe. [PARENT] will check in with [CLIENT] twice per day regarding her symptoms and behaviors in a non-judgmental and non-shaming way. [CLIENT] will seek out [PARENT] if additional check-ins are needed. [CLIENT] will attend her next therapy session in three days to re-assess.

Sample SOAP Note (Blank)

Client: ______________________________

Who Was Present: ______________________________

Session Date and Time: ______________________________

Subjective: ______________________________

Objective: ______________________________

Assessment: ______________________________

Plan: ______________________________

Sample B/P/GIRP Note

Client: [CLIENT] (11-year-old male)

Who Was Present: [CLIENT] for the full session

Session Date and Time: 11/16/2023

Behavior: [CLIENT] is returning to therapy after a one-year break due to emergent stressors in the home. [PARENT] provided updated history and symptom information one week prior to this appointment, and [CLIENT] states he is aware of this. [CLIENT] reports difficulty adjusting to [PARENT]'s significant other moving into the home as well as the significant other's two children staying with them on a week-on, week-off schedule. [CLIENT] states that he likes the significant other but sometimes has conflicts with the children, and he has trouble with continuous changes surrounding who is staying in the home on a given week. [CLIENT] denied aggressive behavior but indicated that they sometimes argue and yell at each other. [CLIENT] also reported that his pet rabbit died two months ago, and he has felt very sad about this. [CLIENT] asked to play a game during the session while discussing these concerns, which has helped increase his comfort in sessions in the past.

Problem: [CLIENT] is returning to therapy after a one-year break due to emergent stressors in the home. [PARENT] provided updated history and symptom information one week prior to this appointment, and [CLIENT] states he is aware of this. [CLIENT] states that he has been having trouble dealing with change as [PARENT]'s significant other moved into the home. He states that he is struggling to get along with the significant other's two children, who are staying with them on a week-on, week-off schedule. [CLIENT] is also struggling with grief about his pet rabbit, who died about two months ago, and he continues to feel very sad about this.

Goal: [CLIENT] is returning to therapy after a one-year break due to emergent stressors in the home. [PARENT] provided updated history and symptom information one week prior to this appointment, and [CLIENT] states he is aware of this. [CLIENT] has been struggling with transitions since [PARENT]'s significant other moved in and the significant other's children have been staying with them on a week-on, week-off schedule. [CLIENT] states that he would like to learn how to get along with them and not yell when he feels angry or has a conflict. He would also like to be able to let [PARENT] know when there is a problem so that adults can intervene instead of trying to handle things himself when he is struggling. [CLIENT] additionally reports ongoing grief about the death of his pet rabbit two months ago and would like to be able to remember the rabbit without feeling so sad much of the time.

Intervention: Updated [CLIENT]'s treatment plan to include goals of processing current life stressors in a therapeutic environment, developing and utilizing appropriate emotion-regulation skills for these stressors, and communicating needs appropriately. [CLIENT] states that he wants to "feel more calm." [CLIENT] explored and processed emotions about the life changes he brought up in session. Engaged in Uno game while discussing stressors to reduce [CLIENT]'s anxiety about certain topics.

Response: At times, [CLIENT] stated that he was "ready to stop talking about this" regarding certain topics, which the therapist said is his choice and reminded him that he can bring them up later when he is ready. [CLIENT] expressed some anxiety about talking about his grief over the loss of a pet, and so the therapist indicated that we could wait to discuss this topic until he is ready. He appeared visibly more relaxed after this. [CLIENT] chose the Uno game as a session activity and appeared to enjoy it. This seemed to help with re-establishing therapeutic rapport as well.

Plan: [CLIENT]'s next session is scheduled in one week. [PARENT] will attend the first part of the session with the client to review the treatment plan together and ensure that both are on the same page regarding goals. The therapist will bring educational materials for [PARENT] about effective communication to be used with [CLIENT].

Sample B/P/GIRP Note (Blank)

Client: ______________________________

Who Was Present: ______________________________

____

Session Date and Time: ______________________________

____

Behavior: ______________________________

____

____

____

____

____

Problem: ______________________________

____

____

____

____

____

Goal: ______________________________

____

____

____

____

____

Intervention: ______________________________

____

____

____

____

____

Response: ____

____

____

____

____

____

Plan: ____

____

____

____

____

____

Sample SOAP Note With Additional Sections

Client: ______________________________

Who Was Present: ______________________________

____

Risk Assessment:

Safety Concern(s): ______________________________

Risk Level: ______________________________

Protective Factors: ______________________________

Details: ______________________________

____

____

Safety Plan: ______________________________

____

____

Brief Mental Status Exam:

Orientation: ______________________________

Appearance: ______________________________

Mood/Affect: ______________________________

Behavior: ______________________________

Any Notable Change: ______________________________

____

____

Session Date and Time: ______________________________

____

Subjective: ______________________________

____

____

____

____

____

Objective: ______________________________

____

____

____

____

____

Assessment: ______________________________

____

____

____

____

____

Plan: ______________________________

____

____

____

____

____

Diagnosis: ______________________________

Changes to Diagnosis: ______________________________

____

____

____

Sample B/P/GIRP Note With Additional Sections

Client: ______

Who Was Present: ______

______

Risk Assessment:

Safety Concern(s): ______

Risk Level: ______

Protective Factors: ______

Details: ______

______

______

Safety Plan: ______

______

______

Brief Mental Status Exam:

Orientation: ______

Appearance: ______

Mood/Affect: ______

Behavior: ______

Any Notable Change: ______

______

______

Session Date and Time: ______

______

Behavior: ______

______

______

______

______

______

Problem: ______

______

Goal:

Intervention:

Response:

Plan:

Diagnosis:

Changes to Diagnosis:

Sample Open-Ended Note

Client: [CLIENT] (14-year-old male)

Who Was Present: [PARENT] individually for 10 minutes; [CLIENT] individually for 25 minutes; [PARENT] and [CLIENT] together for 10 minutes

Session Date and Time: 8/6/2024

Session Content: [PARENT] requested to touch base with the therapist at the start of the session. [PARENT] disclosed that [CLIENT] had "a hard day" at school today. [CLIENT] reportedly became frustrated during math class because he did not want to complete an assignment. When the teacher told [CLIENT] that he needed to keep working, [CLIENT] "blew up," yelled, and threw his textbook across the room. [CLIENT] has had ongoing anger issues in the classroom, but this is the first instance noted where he became physical. [PARENT] wanted the therapist to be aware before the session so that [CLIENT] was not responsible for the disclosure.

Therapist asked [CLIENT] whether he wants to share his perspective of what occurred. [CLIENT] stated that he often tries to "hold in" his anger at school when he does not want to do things, but today he felt "at my limit" and "out of control," leading to the outburst. He and the therapist explored triggers for his anger and engaged in a mindfulness activity to help [CLIENT] notice what anger feels like in his body. Therapist shared a psycho-educational piece about anger and how feelings do not go away when they are held in. [CLIENT] stated that he does not like to express anger because he does not want to be disciplined for feeling angry.

Therapist invited [PARENT] to join at the end of the session to review skills practiced in session and facilitate communication. [PARENT] indicated agreement with the therapist that feeling angry by itself is not a reason why [CLIENT] will get into trouble, but behaviors while angry can lead to discipline if they are inappropriate. [PARENT] stated that they will contact the teacher about this and ensure that the school is also reinforcing this. [PARENT] and [CLIENT] will practice communicating feelings activity together between now and the next session, scheduled for one week from today.

Sample Open-Ended Note (Blank)

Client: ____________________

Who Was Present: ____________________

____

Session Date and Time: ____________________

Session Content: ____________________

Sample Play Therapy Documentation

[Client] and this therapist engaged in non-directive play for the session. Due to [Client's] age and developmental level, this is a developmentally appropriate intervention to allow [Client] to explore her emotions while building rapport with the therapist.

The therapist indicated that [Client] may choose what to play with for today's session. [Client] chose the toy kitchenette and plastic food. The therapist joined [Client] in play, allowing her to guide the session and narrating emotion and themes throughout the session. [Client] crafted detailed recipes using food and items from the kitchen, then pretended to eat the food with the therapist. [Client] made many statements about feeling hunger and the food tasting good. This may tie into her history of food insecurity.

At times, [Client] had the therapist assist her with manipulating the toys a specific way. The therapist used these moments to practice asking for help and appropriate communication skills.

Sample Treatment Summary

[DATE]

Re: [CLIENT name and date of birth]

Dear [REQUESTING PARTY]:

Per your request, I am writing with a treatment summary from my time as [CLIENT]'s therapist. This letter includes a summary of my observation of [CLIENT]'s symptoms and behavior, diagnostic information, and treatment in therapy.

[CLIENT] is a six-year-old male whose parents lived together until he was approximately six months old, when they separated. The parents were never married and presently share joint custody, and [CLIENT] spends one week at a time in each parent's home. This has been the schedule since their separation.

[PARENT 1] initially requested therapy for [CLIENT] and presented for an intake for [CLIENT] on [DATE], approximately two years prior to this treatment summary. At that time, [PARENT 1] stated that she made the appointment due to concerns about [CLIENT] exhibiting anxiety, behavior outbursts, and clinging to her when dropped off at daycare, as well as making statements that he thought she would not return or that he would not see her again. He also reportedly began refusing to sleep by himself approximately six months prior to this intake. [PARENT 1] additionally stated that [CLIENT] returned from [PARENT 2]'s home with a black eye on one occasion, and she was not told a reason for the injury.

When he first presented for therapy, [CLIENT] appeared shy and withdrawn. He indicated that he wanted [PARENT 1] present for his session. He stated that he wanted to leave but was willing to join the session with [PARENT 1] present. In the session, [CLIENT] engaged in play with [PARENT 1] but did not make eye contact with me, respond to me verbally, or acknowledge my presence. When [PARENT 1] indicated she needed to go to the bathroom, [CLIENT] became very agitated and indicated that he needed to go with her.

Based on [PARENT 1]'s report of [CLIENT]'s excessive fear she will not return when she drops him off, co-sleeping, behavioral outbursts when separating from her, and attempts to refuse going to daycare, as well as my observation of [CLIENT]'s behavior in the initial session, I have diagnosed [CLIENT] with Separation Anxiety Disorder.

[PARENT 2] brought [CLIENT] to the second session, and [CLIENT] again requested that his parent join him in the session. [CLIENT] showed [PARENT 2] toys that he had played with in the first session. Initially, [CLIENT] only interacted with [PARENT 2] but allowed me to join in play during the second half of the session.

Since this time, [CLIENT] has had regular weekly sessions with me, with [PARENT 1] and [PARENT 2] bringing him on alternating weeks based on their custody schedule. The parents have cancelled appointments occasionally due to illness or weather, but [CLIENT]'s attendance is good overall. I can provide specific attendance details upon request. Over time, [CLIENT] has slowly established rapport and been willing to engage in play with me. He continues to request that [PARENT 1] join his sessions but meets with me individually approximately half of the time when [PARENT 2] brings him. He continues to check on [PARENT 2] to ensure that he is still in the waiting room two to three times per session when we meet individually.

Due to [CLIENT]'s age and developmental level, I utilize unstructured and non-directive play techniques to help [CLIENT] feel a sense of control in his appointments and to build rapport. He is able to express himself through play and process emotions in the manner that is both comfortable and developmentally appropriate. As he grows and develops improved communication skills, talk therapy and more structured interventions may become appropriate, and his treatment plan will be updated to reflect this. I can provide research around the efficacy of this approach for [CLIENT]'s demographic.

[CLIENT]'s play preferences vary somewhat. He often states that toys are "broken" and uses my first aid kit to "fix" them. Usually, the toy he is "fixing" is not actually broken. When [PARENT 1] attends his session, [CLIENT] often has her care for a baby doll and directs her in what the baby needs and how she ought to take care of it. When [PARENT 2] attends sessions, [CLIENT] often chooses building blocks and directs [PARENT 2] in helping him construct something. Over time, he has involved me more directly in play, including asking for help with activities and giving me roles in his imaginative play.

[PARENT 1] reports that [CLIENT] continues to resist being dropped off at school on transition days (when he knows that [PARENT 2] is picking him up), but they have used the book *Wherever You'll Be* to help increase his comfort being away from her and read it together prior to leaving for school on these days. [PARENT 2] denies that [CLIENT] exhibits anxiety about separating from him at school but has noted that [CLIENT] becomes frustrated and tearful very quickly at home when told no or when he has to wait for something.

I have not observed any injuries to [CLIENT], and [CLIENT] has not made any statements suggesting abuse. No information from [CLIENT]'s sessions has required me to make a report to Child Protective Services.

The information provided here is limited to my observations of [CLIENT] in his sessions, as well as information provided by his parents about behavior and symptoms outside of the therapy setting. My clinical conclusions are based on my professional observations and the information provided to me. If you have any questions about this letter, you can contact me at [CONTACT INFORMATION]. Thank you.

Sincerely,

[Therapist signature, name, and credentials]

Termination Note

Client: [CLIENT] (eight-year-old female)

Date: 3/20/2024

Presenting Problem: [CLIENT] was referred by her primary physician for therapy services due to panic attacks occurring at school and on play dates.

Reason for Termination: [CLIENT] disclosed previously unknown trauma history outside this therapist's scope of practice and has been referred to an appropriate specialist.

Treatment Goals: Initial treatment goals were to reduce panic attacks and increase client's ability to return to locations where panic attacks had occurred in the past.

Diagnosis at Start of Treatment: Provisional diagnosis of F41.0 Panic Disorder due to [CLIENT] reports periods of sweating, shaking, dizziness, and racing heart. [PARENT] has observed these attacks and noted that [CLIENT] also breathes heavily during attacks. [CLIENT] reports not wanting to return to the homes of friends where attacks have occurred. [CLIENT] reportedly resists attending school after a panic attack happens at school. The panic attacks began occurring about two years ago but within the last six months increased in frequency to two to three times per week.

Current Diagnosis: Rule-Out for Post-Traumatic Stress Disorder or another trauma- and stressor-related disorder

Treatment Summary: [CLIENT] was referred for therapy services due to panic attacks. [CLIENT] was seen weekly for three months to treat panic symptoms through individual therapy and therapy involving [PARENT] participation.

Modality and Interventions Used: Cognitive Behavioral Therapy has evidence base in treating Panic Disorder and other anxiety disorders and so was incorporated into [CLIENT]'s treatment plan. Utilized gradual exposure to reduce panic symptoms and increase [CLIENT]'s ability to go places where she has had attacks in the past. Engaged in mindfulness activities for awareness of body sensations and help [CLIENT] identify when her anxiety is starting to rise so that she can use skills before an attack occurs. [PARENT] additionally participated in therapy to help [CLIENT] practice coping skills between sessions and model effective emotion regulation in the home.

Outcome: Two weeks ago, [CLIENT] disclosed to [PARENT] outside of session that [CLIENT]'s panic symptoms began after a sexual assault by a family friend two years ago. [PARENT] reported this to Child Protective Services and law enforcement immediately, and the therapist additionally made a CPS report per mandated reporting requirements. [PARENT] met with this therapist individually (see progress note) and discussed the impact of this information on [CLIENT]'s diagnosis and treatment plan. This therapist informed [PARENT] of the probability that these panic symptoms are a trauma response. This therapist does not specialize in treating trauma-related disorders and believes that it is in [CLIENT]'s best interest to be referred to [PROVIDER], a specialist who works with child sexual abuse survivors.

Next Steps: [PARENT] has provided written release of information for this therapist to communicate with [PROVIDER] about [CLIENT]'s care. [PROVIDER] has indicated availability and willingness to take [CLIENT]'s case. [PARENT] has an intake scheduled with [PROVIDER] next week. [CLIENT] will continue to receive mental health services from [PROVIDER] to treat their trauma and determine accurate diagnosis in light of the additional history information provided.

Termination Note (Blank)

Client: ______________________________

Date: ______________________________

Presenting Problem: ______________________________

____

Reason for Termination: ______________________________

Treatment Goals: ______________________________

____

____

Diagnosis at Start of Treatment: ______________________________

Current Diagnosis: ______________________________

TreatmentSummary: ______________________________

____

____

____

____

____

Modality and Interventions Used: ______________________________

____

____

____

____

____

Outcome: ______________________________

____

____

____

____

____

Next Steps: ______________________________

____

____

____

____

Glossary of Terms

assessment: Evaluating and drawing conclusions about a client based on psychological measures or observable data.

BIRP Note: A progress note format that details information about Behaviors the client presents, Interventions used in the session, the client's Response to these interventions, and the Plan for treatment moving forward.

concurrent: When the therapist completes a progress note during the session with input from the client.

differential diagnosis: When a provider requires additional information to determine which of two or more diagnoses the client may have that present with similar symptoms.

GIRP Note: A progress note format that details information about the client's Goals for the session, Interventions used in the session, the client's Response to these interventions, and the Plan for treatment moving forward.

intervention: An activity incorporated into a session or presented for the client's use between sessions to treat their presenting symptoms.

medically necessary: Any service that is needed to diagnose or treat a client's presenting mental health issues.

non-directive play therapy: A therapeutic approach used with children in which the client takes the lead in session rather than the therapist directing activities.

PIRP Note: A progress note format that details information about the client's presenting Problem, Interventions used in the session, the client's Response to these interventions, and the Plan for treatment moving forward.

play therapy: A therapeutic approach often used with children in which play is used to help the child express and process feelings in a developmentally appropriate way.

process note: Documentation that is not part of the client's medical record, which may include notes taken during session, consultation, or the provider's emotional responses in the session.

progress: Moving toward achieving the goals detailed in the treatment plan.

progress note: A component of the client's medical record that includes details about what occurred in a session.

regression: When symptoms increase or re-emerge after they have been addressed and treated.

rupture: A breakdown in the therapeutic alliance, which may be caused by disagreement between the client and therapist, loss of confidentiality due to a guardian viewing notes, or other loss of rapport between the client and therapist.

SOAP Note: A progress note format that details Subjective (client's report of symptoms), Objective (therapist's observation of client's presentation), Assessment (therapist's conclusions based on subjective and objective information), and Plan (next steps in treatment).

termination note: A note indicating that treatment has ended including information about the progress of treatment.

treatment summary: An overview of a client's treatment, progress, and interventions used.

Works Cited

Arkansas Building Effective Services for Trauma. (2016, April 27). *Trauma-focused cognitive behavioral therapy training – introductory*. Arkansas Building Effective Services for Trauma.

Boyles, O. (2022a, September 8). *Psychotherapy notes vs progress notes – key differences*. ICANotes. www.icanotes.com/2018/06/08/the-differences-between-psychotherapy-notes-and-progress-notes/

Boyles, O. (2022b, September 8). *BIRP notes – complete guide for 2021*. ICANotes. www.icanotes.com/2021/08/18/birp-notes-guide/

Boyles, O. (2022c, September 8). *Pirp vs girp vs BIRP notes – what's the difference?* ICANotes. www.icanotes.com/2021/07/30/pirp-vs-girp-vs-birp-notes/

Cassado-Frankel, T. (2016). Child's play: How play therapy works. *Psychology Today*.

Disla de Jesus, V., Liem, A., Borra, D., & Appel, J. M. (2022). Who's the boss? Ethical dilemmas in the treatment of children and adolescents. *Focus, 20*(2), 215–219. https://doi.org/10.1176/appi.focus.20210037

Landau, R., & Reamer, F. G. (2022, March 30). *Ethics and risk management in behavioral health*. PESI. https://catalog.pesi.com/item/95450/?_gl=1*df1lum*_ga*MTk2NzE5MTg0My4xNjcyMDkzODU2*_ga_JGEX25L44L*MTY3MjA5OTI4NS4yLjEuMTY3MjA5OTY2Ny41My4wLjA.&_ga=2.160416376.41886599.1672093856-1967191843.1672093856

Lees, R. A., Sveen, J. J., Stevens, M. J., & McNally, M. J. (2015). *Process vs. progress notes – Robert A. Lees & associates*. Retrieved December 27, 2022, from www.robertalees.com/wp-content/uploads/sites/6205/2015/05/Process-vs-Progress-Notes.pdf

Podder, V., Lew, V., & Ghassemzadeh, S. (2021). *SOAP notes*. StatPearls Publishing.

Staff. (2019, January 22). Termination: Ending the therapeutic relationship-avoiding abandonment. *NASWCANEWS.org*. Retrieved December 26, 2022, from https://naswcanews.org/termination-ending-the-therapeutic-relationship-avoiding-abandonment/

CHAPTER 9

CONSULTATIONS AND CONTACT NOTES

Intakes, treatment plans, and progress notes are all tied to specific sessions and appointments. But what about when you communicate with a client, their guardian, or another professional outside the session? What if you have an ethical dilemma or are struggling with providing a client with the best possible treatment and need consultation from another provider? This chapter details all the important components of documenting contact notes and professional consultation.

What Is Professional Consultation?

Professional consultation occurs when a mental health professional works with someone else to ensure that a client is getting the best possible treatment. All ethical codes require that providers seek consultation when we need to, and all providers require consultation at some point (Barnett, 2019). Research shows that consultation groups improve provider competency (Bailey et al., 2014).

Therapists can use consultation to talk through and problem-solve when they are having trouble helping a client progress in therapy, when they experience countertransference (strong emotions about the client), or when they have an ethical concern about the case. Often, consultation occurs between multiple mental health professionals who give each other feedback about their clinical work. However, you may sometimes consult with a lawyer when deciding the most appropriate action to take after receiving a subpoena or when you experience another legal issue.

Many providers participate in consultation groups with whom they meet regularly. This makes it easy to seek consultation when needed because the group is already worked into the provider's schedule, they already have trusted colleagues they can turn to, and they are reminded on a regular basis to consider whether consultation may be appropriate. This can be especially beneficial for those who struggle to find the time to engage in consultation (Lyon et al., 2013).

Others simply know which professionals they can turn to when the need for consultation arises. The people you contact for consultation will likely also contact you on a regular basis with their own consultation needs. In this case, you may choose to document the interaction with your colleague, but the responsibility to document the consultation falls on the provider whose client was discussed.

There is not one "right" way to do consultation, but all therapists have an obligation to consult when appropriate to ensure that all clients receive ethical and appropriate treatment.

Consultation Versus Supervision

Supervision hours are required prior to obtaining a license to practice mental health services. Each license has different requirements, and these requirements vary by jurisdiction. Supervision

DOI: 10.4324/9781003316442-9

requirements should be covered as part of graduate training. Additionally, different licenses and state laws have requirements about who can be a supervisor. For example, in some states, anyone who has the license that the supervisee is seeking can be a supervisor. Other states have supervisor registries, and supervisors have to complete specific training or education to supervise and be appropriately credentialed.

When you have a supervisor, you meet with them regularly and have a required number of hours per week where you discuss clients, their treatment, and your professional growth. It is an important part of developing clinical skills and ensuring that clients are receiving adequate and appropriate care. Supervisors typically sign off on any documentation generated by their supervisee and may keep additional supervision notes.

While supervision involves the dynamic of an authority figure (supervisor) teaching someone who answers to them (supervisee), consultation is a discussion between two professionals on equal ground. In addition, a supervisor is responsible for the supervisee's clinical choices and interactions with clients. If a supervisee behaves unethically or inappropriately, the supervisor's license is on the line. With consultation, on the other hand, both parties have their own independent licenses and are not legally or ethically responsible for each other's clinical work. They also have less information about the client and the case presented because providers are responsible for only divulging information that is necessary for the consultation, whereas a supervisor is responsible for reading and signing off on all documentation.

Because consultation is not a relationship where one party has authority over the other, you may choose to disregard the feedback you receive – but it is important to document your reasoning behind this decision. Of course, when you participate in a consultation group, you may receive conflicting feedback. In this case, document the different input you received, what you acted on, and your reasoning for your choice.

Consultation and Client Consent

Consultation should never include divulging information that could be used to identify a client. The information shared is limited to what is necessary for effective consultation and nothing more. Because of this, we are not required to obtain an official release of information prior to obtaining consultation about a client. However, it is good practice to let all clients know that you might bring up their care in consultation. Let them know that, because it is important to ensure they receive the best possible care, you are obligated to seek consolation with other professionals as needed and receive feedback about how you can give them the best possible treatment.

After receiving consultation, you might choose to let your client or their guardian know that you brought their case to consultation. This transparency can help with rapport. It might also be necessary to share that you consulted about a client if there is an ethical or legal issue present, and you can disclose the specific steps you took to make sure you were making the best clinical choices.

If you and another provider have a mutual case (for example, if you see a child individually and another therapist does family therapy with the child and their parents, or if you see an adolescent and another provider sees your client's parent), you might consult with that provider about the case to help with addressing family dynamics and relationships. In this case, you need a release of information and consent from all parties involved, since identifying information is shared. If you are in a general consultation group and realize that you and another provider share a client or family, it is best practice not to consult with that colleague about the case without an appropriate release of information from the legal guardian.

What Information Is Shared?

As noted, consultation should not include information that could be used to identify the client and should only involve sharing the information necessary in order to consult on the case. If you have reason to believe that a colleague may have a connection to your case, you should not consult about that particular case with that colleague. If a colleague brings a consultation to you and you realize you have a connection to the case, you are responsible for letting them know and ending the consultation.

When consulting, share information that is needed in order to get the feedback you require, and nothing more. You must balance the client's right to confidentiality with your duty to seek appropriate consultation, which can be challenging. Be sure to document all information that was shared during the consultation, unless there is a confidentiality or safety concern such as those noted in the previous chapter (progress notes).

When Is Professional Consultation Necessary?

When in doubt, consult. If you feel you are struggling with a client's treatment, feedback from another professional can help. As noted previously, this is an ethical duty for all providers in order to provide the best possible care to our clients. Consultation will often be with other mental health providers, but you may engage in professional consultation with other professionals, such as lawyers.

Specifically, you may want to seek consultation if:

1. You are trying to determine whether you have a dual relationship that requires referring a client out: E.g., rural providers might have to decide between accepting a client who attends their church or asking that client to travel 100 miles to the next closest provider.
2. You are unsure about whether something falls under mandated reporting: E.g., a client may have alluded to abuse but did not give definitive details, and you need to talk out whether you were given enough information to file a report.
3. You received a request for records and are unsure about whether you have appropriate consent: E.g., one parent requests that record be released but the other has declined to authorize release.
4. You are trying to determine whether your feelings about a case have impaired your ability to provide adequate care: E.g., a client has a trauma history very similar to your own, and you are experiencing strong emotions as a result.
5. You are unsure about the applicable laws related to a case. (In this case, you might consult with a lawyer rather than a fellow therapist. Again, only share information essential for conducting the consultation.)
6. You have any uncertainty about your ability to provide ethical or competent care. (You might also have your own therapist – your therapy sessions are *not* consultations even if you are processing stress related to your work. This is your own treatment for your mental health, a service you are paying for and not a professional exchange.)

What Other Types of Contact Happen Outside of Sessions?

Even if you do not feel you need professional consultation for a case, you are likely to have some level of contact with clients, guardians, and others involved in cases outside of sessions. This occurs for various reasons, and providers set various boundaries about how they handle these contacts. There is not one correct way to manage this, but determining what works best for you in your practice is an important part of your job.

The reasons for contact between sessions include:

1. **General check-in:** A parent or other significant adult in your client's life might want to check in about their treatment, get suggestions for how to reinforce treatment goals between sessions, or want to update you about something they have observed.
2. **Changes:** If the client exhibits a sudden change in behavior, it might be important for you to know this before the next session. A parent may also want to update you regarding a change in medication, an IEP at school, or an update regarding other treatment they are receiving.
3. **Crisis:** If a client experiences an immediate crisis, depending on your practice policies, they may reach out to you regarding next steps. For those working in outpatient therapy, you may have a plan in place for steps a client can take in a crisis that do not include calling the therapist directly. In this case, the guardian may still reach out to you after the crisis to let you know what happened. They may also let you know whether a client required hospitalization.
4. **Scheduling:** If the client needs to cancel or reschedule an appointment, they or their guardian might contact you outside of their session.
5. **Coordination of care:** A teacher, speech therapist, occupational therapist, family therapist, prescriber, or other member of a client's treatment team may reach out to you to ensure that care is coordinated in the way that is most beneficial to the client. Always make sure you have an appropriate release of information for this.
6. **Therapist-initiated contact:** The therapist may reach out to the client or their guardian between sessions for a variety of reasons. You may need to reschedule an appointment due to illness or your own emergency, or you may have to let the client know about billing or payment. In addition, you might initiate a conversation with the guardian about changes that can be made in the home or update them about the client's symptoms.

Any contact with or about a client between sessions must be documented and noted in the client's chart.

Boundaries Around Contact Outside of Sessions

Therapists are allowed to have professional boundaries regarding contact between sessions. For example, in my own practice, my clients are given information about local crisis resources prior to the start of treatment rather than my personal contact information. I know that I am a better provider when I am allowed to have "off" time, and so I make sure to give myself space for this. On the other hand, therapists who practice Dialectical Behavioral Therapy allow clients to call them directly between sessions as part of the treatment plan (Vaughn, 2021).

There is not one right way to have boundaries regarding client contact between sessions. Just like each client has different needs, each provider has a different approach to treatment that allows them to work at their best, and we develop boundaries based on what works best for us as individuals (MacMullin et al., 2020). If a client needs more accessibility between sessions than I am able to offer safely and competently, this does not mean they are bad or wrong, just as it does not mean that my boundary is wrong. It simply means that I need to refer them to the right provider to meet their needs.

You will also have boundaries around the type of contact a client can make between sessions. Some providers prefer phone calls, where they can address all concerns in one conversation. Others prefer email, giving them time to consider the best response and allowing them to respond at a time that works for their schedule.

What Information Is Shared in Contacts?

Depending on your jurisdiction, a parent or guardian may have the right to request any information about a client's treatment when they contact you. Be aware both of the guardian's rights and any agreements made as a component of the treatment plan, as well as concerns about the client's safety or protecting your therapeutic relationship with them (Kirkbride, 2018).

In general, providers will share whatever information is necessary and in the client's best interest. For example, they may tell the parent or guardian about specific interventions that can be done in the home, or they may share educational information with a teacher to help them better understand the client's diagnosis.

If the therapist is not authorized to share information with the person contacting them, no information is shared. If, for example, I receive an email or voicemail from someone who is not the client, the legal guardian, or authorized representative, and I do not have consent to contact that person, I will not respond to the contact at all. Some providers will respond to indicate that they are unable to communicate with that person, but the appropriateness of this choice depends on your ethics code. If the client or their legal guardian states that they do not consent for you to communicate with this person, you may not respond to the message.

The one exception to this rule is if the person contacting the provider has a court order that has been signed by a judge. In this case, the provider must alert the client or their guardian that they received the court order and that they are legally required to comply. The provider may contact the judge and request that the order be modified if they have concerns about releasing the requested information, but they are required to respond to and comply with court orders (APA's Committee on Legal Issues, 2016).

Confidentiality With Parents and Guardians

As noted previously, providers, clients, and legal guardians should all be on the same page from the start of treatment regarding confidentiality and what information will or will not be disclosed. If the guardian feels that the limitations of confidentiality should be adjusted, this discussion should include the client as well for transparency.

Releases of Information

As stated earlier, any contact with anyone who is not the client or their legal guardian should include an appropriate release of information. This release includes information about what specific information may be shared and with whom. For example, if a client's school is contacting you regarding setting up an IEP, the guardian may consent to disclosing the client's diagnosis but not information about their ongoing treatment.

A release of information must include a cutoff date in order to be considered HIPAA-compliant. This cutoff may be a specific date or an event (for example, "This release is valid until the end of the school year on June 5, 2023" or "This release is valid until the end of treatment") (U.S. Department of Health and Human Services, 2003). In addition, the legal guardian may rescind a release of information verbally or in writing at any time.

Mandated Reporting

Laws surrounding mandated reporting vary by jurisdiction, and any practicing therapist should be up-to-date and knowledgeable about what they are required to report. This information must be communicated to clients and their guardians at the start of treatment (see Chapter 2).

Jurisdictions have local offices that handle reports of child abuse, neglect, endangerment, and other mandated reporting issues. Often this agency is under the Department of Human Services. If the report is about an imminent danger (for example, the child is in danger by the parent who is taking them home from your session), you may need to call law enforcement to immediately ensure the child's safety. Your report should include documentation of which department you called, why, and with whom you spoke.

Mandated reports fall under professional communications made outside of a session, and therapists need to document when and why a report was made. However, as noted in Chapter 8, sometimes notes included in a client's record are subject to review by the parent or guardian. In the event that you are making a mandated report and the alleged perpetrator is the parent, including this information in the chart may put the child in danger. These notes may be included in a "process notes" file (see Chapter 8) so that they are not released upon request.

If the alleged perpetrator is not the parent or guardian, you may use your clinical judgment in disclosing information about the mandated report. In most jurisdictions, while the reporter may be required to disclose their name and profession when making the report, this information is to be kept confidential to prevent retaliation against a professional who has made a report in good faith. Depending on the circumstances, though, you may choose to let the parent know so that they are aware that the local child protection agency may reach out. If the alleged perpetrator is not the parent but is someone in the home, you may find it is essential to let the parent know in order to create and implement an appropriate safety plan.

It is not within the therapist's role to determine whether an allegation of child abuse is accurate or true. We are rather required to report what we were told and allow the appropriate agency to investigate. We cannot say that we chose not to file a report because we felt the allegation did not have merit, and we are legally protected from retaliation if it turns out that we made a good-faith report based on inaccurate information.

Samples

This chapter includes two sample consultation notes: One with specific prompts and one with more open-ended options to detail what took place in the consultation. In addition, a sample contact note is included. If contact occurs via email, the "note" may consist just of a copy of that email in a document, with any supplemental notes that the provider has about the exchange (for example, if the provider did not disclose certain information, their rationale behind this, or what additional follow-up is planned). Finally, a sample mandated report is included.

Templates can be modified or tweaked to meet individual needs.

Consultation: Details

Date of Consultation: 5/6/2024 Consultation: Dr. [NAME]

Reason for Consultation: Determining appropriate next steps in client's treatment

Demographic Information Shared: 12-year-old girl, adopted at birth. Diagnosed with Fetal Alcohol Spectrum Disorder, history of learning problems. Lives in [CITY] with two adoptive parents, two of the family's biological children, and one other adopted child.

Treatment Information Shared: Parents seeking therapy services due to increased difficulty with emotion regulation, aggressive behavioral outbursts, and not completing schoolwork. Client has been attending sessions for a few months, and therapist feels "stuck."

Consult Recommendations: Consider additional evaluation for possible overlooked comorbidities due to behaviors and learning issues being attributed to FASD. Emphasize attachment work in treatment to improve parent-child connection, communication.

Provider Next Steps: Provide referral for evaluation. Re-evaluate treatment plan with client and parent input for attachment-based care.

Was the client/guardian informed of this consultation? O Yes O No

Reason: Therapist informed client and parents about this consultation in advance as a resource to ensure the therapist is providing the best possible care.

Consultation: Details (Blank)

Date of Consultation: ______________________ Consultation: ______________________

Reason for Consultation: ______________________

____

Demographic Information Shared: ______________________

____

____

Treatment Information Shared: ______________________

____

____

Consult Recommendations: ______________________

____

____

Provider Next Steps: ______________________

____

____

Was the client/guardian informed of this consultation? O Yes O No

Reason: ______________________

____

Consultation: Open-Ended

Date of Consultation: ______________________ Consultation: ______________________

Note: Met with Dr. [NAME] for consultation regarding [CLIENT], age nine. In his most recent session, [CLIENT] reported that [PARENT] has engaged in discipline practices that may fall under mandated reporting. Therapist required feedback in making decisions about best practice for reporting, confidentiality, and ongoing care that follows [STATE] laws and the ethics code. Disclosed information from the session to Dr. [NAME]: [CLIENT] stated that, when he gets into trouble at school, [PARENT] punishes him by withholding dinner. This occurs about twice per week per [CLIENT]'s report. The therapist and [PARENT] have discussed appropriate discipline, and [PARENT] previously had a CPS investigation for using corporal punishment. [CLIENT] reports that [PARENT] has stopped using physical punishment and has not been physical with him. [STATE] law indicates that physical abuse falls under mandated reporting, but neglect does not. Dr. [NAME] noted that deliberate withholding of food goes beyond neglect, as [PARENT] has means available but chooses not to allow [CLIENT] to eat. Therapist will provide a report to Child Protective Services and refer [PARENT] to positive discipline class.

Consultation: Open-Ended (Blank)

Date of Consultation: ____________________ Consultation: ____________________

Note: ____________________

Contact Note

Client: [CLIENT

Date: 11/16/2024

Contact Person: Ms. T

Relationship to Client: Teacher

Method of Contact Phone call

Time in Minutes: 15

Charge for Contact: O Yes O No

Amount N/A

Reason for Contact: IEP Update

Details: Ms. T called in advance of [CLIENT]'s IEP meeting tomorrow. Ms. T requested treatment update for [CLIENT]. [PARENT] has signed a release of information for the therapist to speak to Ms. T for this purpose. Ms. T verified [PARENT]'s report that [CLIENT] has shown improved ability to remain in the classroom and engage with learning but continues to struggle with grades, particularly in math. Discussed possible learning disorder evaluation. Ms. T indicated that [SCHOOL] is working on a referral for this. Reviewed coping skills [CLIENT] has practiced in sessions so that Ms. T can cue [CLIENT] if she notices he is struggling. Therapist encouraged Ms. T to present these prompts in a non-judging, non-shaming manner and to cue [CLIENT] without bringing peers' attention. Ms. T will call with additional questions if needed and will fax a copy of the updated IEP when it is complete.

Contact Note (Blank)

Client: ______________________ Date: ______________________

Contact Person: ______________________ Relationship to Client: ______________

Method of Contact: ______________________ Time in Minutes: ______________

Charge for Contact: O Yes O No Amount: ______________________

Reason for Contact: ____

Details: ____

____

____

____

____

____

____

____

____

____

____

Sample Mandated Report

Client: [Client] Date: March 5, 2024

Reporting Agency: CPS Agent: [Agent]

Report: In [Client's] session today, he made a statement alleging child abuse. [Client] stated that [Parent 1]'s new boyfriend often yells at him, and over the weekend, he struck [Client] on the head with an open hand twice because he felt that [Client] was not listening or responding to a command quickly enough. There were no visible marks on [Client], though the nature of the altercation would not necessarily leave a bruise. This therapist contacted CPS and spoke with [Agent], providing [Client]'s demographic information. This therapist informed [Agent] of the allegation made by [Client]. [Agent] stated that an investigation will be opened. [Client] additionally stated that [Parent 1] would be "really mad at me" if [Parent 1] became aware that [Client] told this therapist about the altercation. [Client] stated that [Parent 1] has not physically hurt him, but [Parent 1] often "gets really mad and yells and screams so loud it hurts my ears" when he is in trouble. Due to these safety concerns, this therapist did not inform [Parent 1] of this report and informed [Agent] of [Client's] concerns about [Parent 1] knowing that he told his therapist about the altercation. This note will be kept out of [Client's] official chart due to this safety concern.

Sample Mandated Report (Blank)

Client: ____________________ Date: ____________________

Reporting Agency: ____________________ Agent: ____________________

Report: ____________________

Glossary of Terms

boundaries: In mental health, refers to limits set for personal well-being and mental health.

consultation: When a professional assists in treatment planning and care to ensure quality, ethical treatment.

contact: Communication between the therapist and client, guardian, or other important adult, with appropriate consent.

countertransference: The therapist's emotional reaction to the client.

court order: A decision or order given by a judge, which must be followed.

mandated reporting: Individuals in certain professions, including therapists, are required to document and report specific abuse, including child abuse.

release of information: Written authorization for the therapist to communicate with someone else about a client, their treatment, or other information about their care.

supervision: A formal, contractual agreement where a more experienced, licensed therapist oversees another therapist's caseload. Supervision is typically required as a component of getting licensed.

transference: The client's emotional reaction to the therapist.

Works Cited

APA's Committee on Legal Issues. (2016). Protecting patient privacy when the court calls. *Monitor on Psychology*. Retrieved November 27, 2022, from www.apa.org/monitor/2016/07-08/ce-corner

Bailey, R., Bell, K., Kalle, W., & Pawar, M. (2014). Restoring meaning to supervision through a peer consultation group in rural Australia. *Journal of Social Work Practice, 28*(4), 479–495.

Barnett, J. E. (2019). The ethical practice of psychotherapy: Clearly within our reach. *Psychotherapy, 56*(4), 431–440. https://doi.org/10.1037/pst0000272

Kirkbride, R. (2018). *Counselling children and young people in private practice: A practical guide*. Routledge.

Lyon, A. R., Ludwig, K., Romano, E., Leonard, S., Stoep, A. V., & McCauley, E. (2013). "If it's worth my time, I will make the time": School-based providers' decision-making about participating in an evidence-based psychotherapy consultation program. *Administration and Policy in Mental Health and Mental Health Services Research, 40*(6), 467–481.

MacMullin, K., Jerry, P., & Cook, K. (2020). Psychotherapist experiences with telepsychotherapy: Pre COVID-19 lessons for a post COVID-19 world. *Journal of Psychotherapy Integration, 30*(2), 248–264. https://doi.org/10.1037/int0000213

U.S. Department of Health and Human Services. (2003). *Must an authorization include an expiration date?* (FAQ 476). Office for Civil Rights. www.hhs.gov/hipaa/for-professionals/faq/476/must-an-authorization-include-an-expiration-date/index.html

Vaughn, S. (2021). *DBT in practice: Mastering the essentials*. Psychotherapy Academy. https://psychotherapyacademy.org/dbt-training-online/

CHAPTER 10

RISK ASSESSMENTS AND SAFETY PLANS

As a graduate student, the scariest thing that might happen in a session was that a client might share that they were thinking about or planning to hurt themselves or someone else. It felt impossible to do all the right things to ensure their safety and make sure that my documentation appropriately reflected that. I hope I can prevent some of that anxiety by addressing risk assessments, safety planning, and documentation in this chapter.

What Is a Risk Assessment?

Our first job as therapists is to keep our clients safe. Secondary to that, we must always thoroughly document how we did this. A risk assessment is how we screen clients for safety, both their own and that of those around them. A thorough intake interview will always include a risk assessment, and progress notes often include a brief risk assessment.

A risk assessment consists of questions about various aspects of safety, both the client's and that of those around them. It is important to document risk assessments both to ensure that appropriate precautions are taken and to show steps you took to ensure your client's safety.

You may not have to ask all risk-assessment questions at every appointment. If a client has no history of aggressive behavior, you do not necessarily need to spend time in every session asking them whether they are thinking about hurting someone. However, if they mention a new symptom or behavior that you think might suggest they are having these thoughts, it can be a good idea to ask. If a client has a history of these thoughts, you might decide it is good practice to check your risk assessment each week to determine whether you need to change your approach or update the safety plan.

With children and teens, a risk assessment often includes questions for the client as well as for the parent or guardian. This ensures that you collect all available information. The parent or guardian might be able to let you know if a client has talked about self-harm behavior when the client does not yet feel comfortable sharing the information directly, so you can be aware of what is going on without pushing them to talk about this before they are ready. On the other hand, the client might share information with you that the parent or guardian is not aware of. If you meet with the parties separately, there might be information they are willing to share individually that they might not share with the other present. (If this is the case, make sure you have addressed any confidentiality limitations. If a parent thinks you will tell them about a client's self-harm and you do not, this could lead to a serious rupture of trust at best and a complaint against your license at worst. Similarly, if a client believes that everything they say is confidential, and you later disclose a safety concern to the parent, the client will be unlikely to trust you again in the future. More information about confidentiality agreements is available in Chapter 4.)

A risk assessment includes information about the nature and severity of various safety risks. It additionally includes the clinician's professional opinion about level of risk and recommendations for next steps. The clinician will note the client's next steps and how these steps are clinically indicated.

DOI: 10.4324/9781003316442-10

Some clinicians feel nervous about risk assessments because they worry they will put the idea in a client's head. It is important to remember that asking about things like self-harm and suicide do not cause someone who is not having these thoughts to suddenly start to feel this way (Dazzi et al., 2014), but someone who feels this way might not be sure how to bring up the topic and may need the provider to ask these questions before they feel safe disclosing. Because of this, risk assessments are not only safe but necessary for thorough clinical assessment.

While we unfortunately cannot guarantee 100% prevention of any and every client safety concern, harm, or even death, how we conduct and document risk assessments can ensure that we follow best practices to keep clients safe. Just like an oncologist cannot ensure that 100% of their patients survive after a diagnosis of cancer, we cannot prevent, predict, and heal every possible aspect of our clients' risk, but we can take steps to keep them as safe as possible.

What Questions Are in a Risk Assessment?

While you may change the wording of various questions based on the client's developmental level, the goal in a risk assessment is to determine ways in which a client might be unsafe. There are several different areas to consider when conducting a risk assessment.

Self-Harm

Self-harm is any behavior that could hurt or injure an individual. Self-harm behaviors are behaviors engaged in with the specific intent of causing hurt or injury. For instance, a teen who cuts themselves or a child who hits their head against the wall during a meltdown is engaging in self-harm behavior.

The following are some areas a provider should consider and ask about when assessing for self-harm:

1. If the client states that they have thoughts of self-harm, what kind of thoughts are these? Does the client *want* to hurt themselves, or are they experiencing distressing, intrusive thoughts that they might hurt themselves, as can occur with obsessive-compulsive disorder? (Someone who has distressing, intrusive thoughts about hurting themselves and states that they do not want to act on these thoughts are typically not at risk for acting out the thoughts, though addressing the thoughts is an important part of treatment.)
2. If the client states that they think about hurting themselves, and they want to act on these thoughts, this is active ideation. The provider must determine whether they intend to act on this desire, what they want to do, and the level of danger and risk associated with the behavior if they act on it.
3. If the client wants to act on a self-harm thought, do they have access to the means necessary to do so? What is the level of risk that they will act on these behaviors?
4. What is the client's history of self-harm behavior? What behaviors have they done in the past with intent to hurt themselves, if any?
5. What precautions and protective factors are in place or could be put in place to ensure the client's safety?

Suicide

Suicidal ideation refers to when an individual is having thoughts of suicide, or a behavior with the intent of ending their life. It is important to differentiate suicidal ideation from self-harm ideation, as many individuals who think about or engage in self-harm behavior do not want to die, and many who experience suicidal ideation do not have a history of self-harm ideation or behavior.

When assessing suicide risk, there are similar questions and considerations to the self-harm assessment, including:

1. What kind of thoughts is the client having? Are they passively thinking, "I wish I were dead?" Are they having intrusive thoughts about death that they find distressing?
2. If the thoughts are active, does the client have a plan about how they would attempt to end their life? What are the specifics of this plan? Sometimes, children who experience suicidal ideation have ideas that are not lethal. For example, a child might state that they want to die, and they plan to hold their breath until it kills them. Never tell a child that their plan would be ineffective, but this information is essential for safety planning purposes.
3. If the thoughts are active and the client has a plan that is potentially lethal, do they have access to the means to act out this plan?
4. What is the client's level of risk for acting on these thoughts?
5. Has the client had suicidal behavior in the past? What did they do, and what happened afterward?
6. What is the guardian's perception of the client's ideation? Do they take these statements seriously? How committed is the guardian to taking steps to protecting the client's safety?
7. What precautions are in place to protect the client's safety?

Risk-Taking or Reckless Behavior

This includes behaviors where a client might not deliberately intend to hurt themselves or end their life, but they are also not taking appropriate precautions to ensure that they remain safe. This might include unsafe substance use, driving, or other risky behaviors.

1. What potentially dangerous behaviors does the client engage in? Do they ever do things that make others worry that they could get hurt, even if they are not trying to?
2. How risky are these behaviors? How seriously could the client be injured engaging in this behavior? Could they die?
3. What is the client's reported level of insight into the behaviors? Do they recognize that they are potentially putting themselves in harm's way, or do they feel it is "not a big deal"?
4. What is the parent or guardian's perception of the behavior? What steps has the parent or guardian taken to protect the client?

Harm to Others

This refers to when a client has thoughts or intent to hurt another person. Mandated reporting laws around "duty to warn" vary by state, but there is case-law precedent holding therapists civilly liable if a client threatens to hurt someone (Tarasoff v. Regents of the University of California, 1976). This means, depending on your jurisdiction, you might have a legal requirement to report a threat of harm to another person, and even if you do not have a legal obligation, failure to report might mean you have civil liability if the client acts on this threat.

1. Again, what are the specifics of the thoughts? Does the client want to harm someone, or do they worry about intrusive thoughts of hurting someone?

2. If they do want to hurt someone, are they expressing anger, or do they have intent to act on this desire?
3. Who do they want to hurt? Can you identify the victim? If not, you may still be obligated to contact law enforcement about the threat for investigation and safety.
4. Is it physically possible for the client to act on this ideation? For example, a client in an long-term inpatient program may not be physically able to contact or access the target of their ideation.
5. Again, what is the guardian's awareness about the client's ideation? Do they take it seriously? What steps have they taken or are they willing to take?

Abuse, Neglect, and Exploitation

This category differs from the others listed because it indicates that the client is at risk of being harmed by another person or has been harmed by another person. In the United States, every jurisdiction requires reporting the abuse of a child, though the legal definition of abuse varies from state to state.

If the legal guardian is the perpetrator, this makes ensuring safety more difficult. A client may disclose a safety concern by the parent, or a parent who lacks the knowledge or resources to understand that their behavior is abusive might disclose the information. Again, it is not the therapist's responsibility to determine the accuracy of an abuse allegation – this is the job of the agency we report to.

Assessing for risk when the parent or guardian has acted abusively is challenging because many people get defensive when presented with the possibility that their behavior was harmful. People want to see themselves as good and want to be able to stand by their choices, so many will hold onto the belief that a behavior was actually *not* harmful rather than wrestle with the realization that they have done something abusive. Additionally, parental neglect is often the result of lack of resources rather than malicious intent. Many parents who experience housing or food insecurity are wonderful parents who simply do not have the means to provide.

Questions must be worded carefully to ensure client safety, gather accurate information, and prevent irreparable rupture to the clinician's rapport with the parent. Questions for the guardian include:

1. What does discipline look like in your household? What punishments or consequences are used, what do they look like, and how often do you find that each type of consequence is necessary?
2. Have you ever left a mark on your child when disciplining them? What happened?
3. Has your family ever lacked necessary resources for your child's needs to be met, and how did you handle this?
4. It sounds like there might be the possibility that you might not have access to these resources in the future (include specific details about this concern, such as lost job, threat of eviction, et cetera). What needs to happen to ensure that your child is safe and has appropriate care? (You may be able to connect them with a referral for this care!)

When asking a child about these concerns, be sure to query as needed to get specific information. Double check and make sure that the client understands what you are asking and that you understand the information they are giving you. Once, a physician colleague of mine called Child Protective Services because they asked the client, "Do you feel safe at home?" and the client answered, "No." It turned out that the client had seen a news story about a break-in and felt unsafe due to worries this could happen at their house. The client, their siblings, and their parents experienced significant distress when the child protection agency sent law enforcement to do a wellness check at the home. Ask the child what they mean or what causes them to feel unsafe to determine whether they are disclosing an abuse allegation or anxiety.

Questions for the child or adolescent can include (with developmentally appropriate modifications as needed):

1. Has an adult ever put their hands on you in a way that hurt or left a mark?
2. Has an adult ever made you afraid they would hurt you in a physical way?
3. What do disagreements look like in your house?
4. What happens when you are in trouble?
5. Have you ever felt like there would not be enough food in your home?
6. Has anything in your house made you feel unsafe? What? What did your parents do about this?

With each of these questions, if the client answers yes, query for more information in an open-ended way.

What Is a Safety Plan?

A safety plan is exactly what it sounds like: A plan to ensure a client's safety. It is something that the provider develops in collaboration with the client and their guardian and includes information about potential safety risks, when they may come up, and how the client can respond to them. It includes details about resources, coping skills, or steps the client and their family can take in response to a safety issue to prevent harm.

A good safety plan also considers the client's willingness and ability to take specific steps. If a client is unable or states that they do not feel they would be willing to follow a step in the safety plan, it is not helpful to include that step.

Safety plans can reduce the need for higher level of care or hospitalization. While sometimes clients need hospitalization to stabilize a crisis or ensure their physical safety, a hospitalization can be highly stressful and even traumatic. One benefit of working with minor clients is that there is an adult responsible for their care outside of your session. You, your client, and their guardian may be able to appropriately ensure safety without hospitalization.

Safety Contracts Versus Safety Plans

A safety contract is a non-binding, non-legal document that a provider has a client sign stating that they will not engage in an unsafe behavior. Clinicians may use safety contracts to cover liability, as a client is essentially promising them that they will remain safe. If a client signs a safety contract but does not follow it (engages in the harmful behavior), the hope is that the contract eliminates the clinician's liability for not keeping the client safe. However, research shows that safety contracts are ineffective in preventing harm and are not therapeutically beneficial (Garvey et al., 2009).

Basically, we know safety contracts do not increase the client's safety, so in the event of civil litigation, the fact that we used an intervention that is known to not be beneficial might be used against us. Additionally, making the client sign a safety contract could interfere with the therapeutic relationship. The client might feel like they cannot disclose that they were unsafe after signing a contract, as they might worry that they let the therapist down or that the therapist will be angry or disappointed in them for "violating" the contract.

A safety plan, on the other hand, empowers the client to make a commitment to their safety in a way that meets their needs and fits with their current values and goals. Safety plans have an evidence base suggesting that they can prevent or reduce harm significantly (Clarke et al., 2019).

Special Considerations for Children and Teens

The frontal lobe of the brain regulates impulse control and decision making. Since this part of the brain does not develop until into adulthood, children and teens are more impulsive than adults. When conducting a risk assessment, clinicians need to take this information into account and make clinical decisions based on the knowledge that children and teens are more likely to act on an impulse when it comes up, such as a suicidal thought or risky behavior.

On the other hand, as noted already, minors have legal guardians who are tasked with protecting them and keeping them safe. Unlike an adult, who may live alone, minor clients go home with adults who might be able to implement a safety plan there. Home is not always a safe place for clients, of course, and if the safety concern is about parental abuse, the fact that the client lives with their parent is not an asset. However, if a client reports they are at risk for suicide, an involved, engaged guardian can often implement a safety plan that could prevent the need for inpatient care.

Always document your professional opinion, clinical decision, and factors that you considered. In addition, documentation should include the recommended next steps and your rationale behind these decisions.

Mandated Reporting

In America, every state has laws about mandated reporting and requirements that certain professionals disclose allegation or suspicion of child maltreatment (Child Welfare Information Gateway, 2019). Specifics vary by state, including what is considered abuse, but many states also require report of alleged or suspected abuse of elders or vulnerable adults, threats of self-harm, and threats to harm someone else.

It is every provider's ethical responsibility to know and understand the mandated reporting requirements where they practice. If you are licensed in multiple states, you must keep track of all relevant laws for each jurisdiction. Furthermore, laws change, and each provider is responsible for staying up-to-date on their reporting requirements. It may help to keep a spreadsheet.

If a risk assessment reveals safety concerns that fall under mandated reporting, you must document both the reported concern and your contact with the appropriate agency. This contact can be done using the contact note guidelines discussed in Chapter 9.

When documenting a mandated reporting issue, be sure to note who is aware that you made the report and why. If, for example, a child alleges that their parent is abusing them, you are required to report this. If the child expresses fear of what the parent will do if the parent knows about the disclosure, it would be unsafe and therefore unethical to tell the parent that you are making a mandated report. (See Chapter 8 for more details about documenting when the legal guardian is the alleged perpetrator.) Include in your documentation that you did not share this information with the parent and why, and let the reporting agency know this as well. Mandated reports are confidential, and the agency should not disclose who made the report when they investigate the claim (Child Welfare Information Gateway, 2019).

Privacy Versus Relationship

Therapeutic rapport is essential for clients to make progress in therapy (Leach, 2005), a fact that is especially true for children and teens. Trust is a huge part of rapport, and a client is very unlikely to trust a therapist if they do not believe that the content of their sessions will be kept confidential. When it comes to safety concerns, though, providers are often required by law and by our ethical codes to breach confidentiality.

Be honest and upfront with clients about any limitations to their confidentiality. Let them know at a developmentally appropriate level what information will and will not be shared and with whom. If you are not honest with your client about a disclosure, there is a risk that they will find out that you made the disclosure and did not share this information with them. This will not only hurt their relationship with you but could cause them to mistrust future providers.

Clients may not want you to disclose safety concerns. This is understandable and natural! In my practice, I tell my clients exactly what is being disclosed and emphasize that I am only doing this to protect their safety. I give details about all the things that will and will not be reported. I also let them know that it is understandable and acceptable if they feel angry with me or worry that they might not trust me in the future. I say, "Of course I want you to like me and trust me, but most of all I need you to be safe. I am okay with you being upset with me if it means you're safe."

Following a rupture of trust, I let the client know again that their feelings toward me are valid and okay, even if I made the correct decision to keep them safe. I tell them that it is okay if they feel like I have broken their trust, and I work to earn their trust back at a pace that is comfortable for them.

This is then an ongoing discussion as we re-establish rapport following the disclosure. You cannot guarantee that a client will be able to recover from a rupture caused by a disclosure, but you can take steps to make sure that the client is alive to have the opportunity to do so. Often, after a crisis has passed, a client will better understand the reason behind the disclosure. Sometimes, they even express gratitude that you prioritized their safety.

Risk Assessments and Trauma

Risk assessments and safety concerns can be challenging for clinicians as well as clients, and clients who have survived traumas often struggle with these issues in specific ways. If the client does not want the safety concern disclosed, they may feel a sense of losing control, which is a feeling that many trauma survivors face. If their trauma involves the medical system, hospitalization could be re-traumatizing and do more harm than good.

Risk assessments should include information about a client's trauma history, if applicable, and how the clinician ensured that their approach to care was trauma-informed. If the trauma history impacted treatment decisions (for example, a client may be at higher risk for self-harm due to trauma-induced dissociative symptoms, or a client might be at risk for triggers in a hospital setting), this should be noted as well.

What Goes Into a Safety Plan?

A thorough safety plan has specific components, which of course can be adjusted and tweaked based on the client's needs and expressed goals. The parts of a safety plan include:

1. **Participants.** Who is involved in the development of the safety plan? Who is aware of the safety plan and involved in making sure it is implemented?

2. **Specific risks.** What behaviors or safety concerns led to the creation of this safety plan? What are you concerned would happen if the safety plan were not followed?
3. **Protective factors.** What is already in place that reduces the client's risk? What has kept them safe so far?
4. **Potential triggers.** What kinds of things could cause the client's risk level to increase suddenly? What should the client and their guardian be on the lookout for?
5. **Coping skills/de-escalation.** What are the client's options in the moment when they are triggered? This section should include very specific steps they will take. It is helpful to have multiple options here, but balance this with not overwhelming them. They should have a few tools to choose from in the moment. Coping skills should be options that are always available to the client and not something they need to ask permission to access or might not have with them in the moment.
6. **Safe people**. Have a list of people the client can reach out to if they experience a crisis. This should include several options, as a given person cannot be expected to be on call continuously. This can also include crisis hotline information.
7. **Worst-case scenario.** What is the plan if the coping skills are not working and there is an immediate safety concern? At what point is hospitalization necessary? What exact steps will be taken in this scenario?
8. **Communication plan.** Guardians understandably often want to frequently check in with the client about their mental state and level of risk, and this can be overwhelming. On the other hand, clients might feel shy or ashamed to share that they are struggling. Balance having trusted adults checking in and giving the client space to breathe. Again, be specific.
9. **Preventative steps.** What will the guardian do to make the home safer? They are not turning the home into a lockdown unit, but if, for example, knives are a trigger for the client, these can be locked up. Have the client share their feelings about the preventative steps taken and empower them to state what they need in order to stay safe.

Harm Reduction

Harm reduction refers to taking steps to ensure that clients make the safest possible choice based on their available resources and personal goals. It can be tempting to push for a client to commit to the safest possible option, but if a client is not in a place where they are able or willing to do this, they are less likely to follow through with a safety plan. Harm reduction means listening to the client and getting information from them about their ability to make small changes to increase safety.

If, for example, a client cannot commit to fully stopping drug use, you can work with them to create a harm reduction-based safety plan in which they agree to use only in a safe location. A client who engages in cutting behavior might not feel able to stop completely, but they may be willing to commit to using a sanitary blade to prevent infection.

Many providers feel uncomfortable with harm reduction because it seems they are "encouraging" a harmful behavior, when in fact they are encouraging clients to make manageable changes at their own pace. There is a large body of evidence about the benefits of harm reduction, particularly around substance use (Levengood et al., 2021).

As with other aspects of care, make sure that you provide education to your client and their guardian or guardians about harm reduction if you are using it in your therapeutic approach. Just like providers might be hesitant to "condone" a potentially risky behavior, parents might balk at the concept of harm reduction since they want to protect their child from any kind of harm. Parents might be able to get behind the concept of harm reduction if it is explained in terms they understand and they have the space to ask questions or express concerns. This might be a conversation to have without the client present so that it does not seem that you are correcting the parent or telling them they are wrong.

Risk Level

Risk level refers to how likely it is that a client will come to harm due to a safety concern. Typically, risk level is documented as not applicable, low, moderate, or high. The higher the risk, the more involved the safety plan should be to protect the client.

"Not applicable" can refer to risk level related to ideation from intrusive thoughts that the client does not want to act on. Technically, a client experiencing intrusive thoughts of harming their loved ones has ideation to harm others, but they are not at risk for acting on these thoughts.

"Low risk" refers to a client who is not necessarily disturbed by their thoughts but has no plan, means, or intent to act on them. A client who expresses that they do not want to take steps to end their life but who finds themselves wishing they were dead is at low risk.

"Moderate risk" is indicated when a client has ideation that they want to act on, but they may not have the means to do so. It can also mean when a client whose ideation is low risk has other factors in place, like poor impulse control, which could cause them to act on their thoughts within a short time period.

"Severe risk" indicates when a client, in the provider's professional opinion, is likely or very likely be unsafe. This could be because their living situation is unsafe or because they have plan, means, and intent to engage in a dangerous behavior. Severe risk means that the clinician must take immediate steps to mitigate the risk and document how they kept their client safe.

Hospitalizations

Inpatient psychiatric care is a tool that can be used to keep a client physically safe while they experience a mental health crisis or make necessary adjustments to treatment or medications under close supervision. There are times when hospitalization is the only option to keep a client safe, and at those times, this referral is necessary even when it is not the preferred option.

At the same time, no tool is right for every job. There are times when hospitalization can be unhelpful or, worse, actively harmful. If hospitalization is necessary to keep a client safe, then the clinician absolutely must make this referral. At the same time, as with safety contracts, sometimes clinicians will err on the side of hospitalizing a client to protect their own liability without fully considering whether this decision is in the client's best interests. A good analogy is surgery: It is never good to cut into someone's body, and all surgeries have recovery time, but if your appendix is inflamed, the safest thing is to take it out.

Adult clients might need to agree to go to the hospital unless you can obtain a court order mandating treatment or an involuntary hold. With minors, whether they agree with the decision to hospitalize or not, a legal guardian can consent on their behalf in many cases. This can simplify the process if the parent agrees that their child is unsafe.

Carefully consider if and when a hospitalization will benefit the client. Document what options you considered and why this was the most appropriate choice in your professional opinion. When a client is hospitalized, the hospital and treatment team might need access to your records.

In an emergency where the records are essential in ensuring the client receives appropriate care, you might not have time to get appropriate written consent and can document verbal consent instead. However, whenever possible, written consent is ideal. Additionally, as soon as you are able, let the client know what was disclosed.

Samples

This chapter includes a sample risk assessment with specific prompts that a provider must screen and open-ended space to provide details about the risk. You might find both beneficial based on the situation. As always, you can choose what system best fits your needs and professional style.

Sample Risk Assessment: Check Boxes

Self-Harm

O Ideation O Plan O Means O Intent

Risk Level

O Not Applicable O Low O Moderate O High

Severity

O Low O Moderate O High

Additional Information: ____________________

____

Suicide

X Ideation X Plan O Means O Intent

Risk Level

O Not Applicable O Low O Moderate X High

Severity

OLow X Moderate O High

Additional Information: Client reported thoughts of wanting to die with a plan to overdose on prescription medication when home alone after school. The parents have OTC medication in the home.

Risk-Taking/Reckless Behavior

Harm to Others

Potential Victim: ____________________

____

Details: ____________________

____

O Ideation O Plan O Means O Intent

Risk Level

O Not Applicable O Low O Moderate O High

Severity

O Low O Moderate O High

Additional Information: ____________________

____

Abuse, Neglect, and Exploitation

Type of Mistreatment: Client reports fear she will be "yelled at" if she discloses suicidal ideation to her parents. Potential emotional abuse in the home.

Risk Level

O Not Applicable X Low O Moderate O High

Severity

X Low O Moderate O High

Additional Information: Parent agrees about maintaining a safety plan in the home. Emotional abuse does not fall under mandated reporting in this state, but provider will provide parenting class information.

Other

Risk: ____

O Ideation O Plan O Means O Intent

Risk Level

O Not Applicable O Low O Moderate O High

Severity

O Low O Moderate O High

Additional Information: ______________________________

Actions Taken

O *Mandated Report*

Agency: ____________________

Contact Person: ____________________

Details Provided: ______________________________

Follow-up Needed: ______________________________

O *Duty to Warn*

O Potential Victim

O Law Enforcement

O Other: ______________________

X *Disclosure to Guardian:* Created safety plan to ensure the client is fully supervised in the home. Parent will keep all medications in a safe to which the client does not have the combination. Parent will take client to [Hospital] if they feel they cannot maintain safety.

O *Disclosure to Another Provider:* Release of Information signed for [Hospital] so that providers can communicate if the client requires inpatient care.

O *Other Disclosure:* ______________________

X *Safety Plan (Attached)*

O *Other Action Taken:* ______________________

Sample Risk Assessment: Check Boxes (Blank)

Self-Harm

O Ideation O Plan O Means O Intent

Risk Level

O Not Applicable O Low O Moderate O High

Severity

O Low O Moderate O High

Additional Information: ______________________________

____

Suicide

O Ideation O Plan O Means O Intent

Risk Level

O Not Applicable O Low O Moderate O High

Severity

O Low O Moderate O High

Additional Information: ______________________________

____

Risk-Taking/Reckless Behavior

Harm to Others

Potential Victim: ______________________________

____

Details: ______________________________

____

O Ideation O Plan O Means O Intent

Risk Level

O Not Applicable O Low O Moderate O High

Severity

O Low O Moderate O High

Additional Information: ______________________________

____

Abuse, Neglect, and Exploitation

Type of Mistreatment: ____

____

Risk Level

O Not Applicable   X Low   O Moderate   O High

Severity

X Low   O Moderate   O High

Additional Information: ____

____

Other

Risk: ____

____

O Ideation   O Plan   O Means   O Intent

Risk Level

O Not Applicable   O Low   O Moderate   O High

Severity

O Low   O Moderate   O High

Additional Information: ____

____

Actions Taken

O *Mandated Report*

Agency: ____________________

Contact Person: ____________________

Details Provided: ____

____

____

Follow-up Needed: ____

____

O *Duty to Warn*

O Potential Victim

O Law Enforcement

O Other: ______________________

O *Disclosure to Guardian:* ______________________

____

O *Disclosure to Another Provider:* ______________________

____

O *Other Disclosure:* ______________________

____

X *Safety Plan (Attached)*

O *Other Action Taken:* ______________________

____

Sample Safety Plan

Participants

Client, mother, father, therapist

Specific Risks

O Self-Harm X Suicide O Dangerous Behavior O Harm to Others O Risk for Abuse

Protective Factors

O Supportive people: Parents, coach, friends

O Something I'm looking forward to: Visiting grandma next month

O A goal I have: Make it to state

O Something important to me: My dog

Potential Triggers

If I see the pills, I might want to take them. If my parents yell at me, I might feel triggered.

Risk Factors

X Specific plan or ideation X Accessible means O History (This has happened before.)

O Impulse control O Lack of support O Triggers

More information: Parents state commitment to keeping the means (medication) locked where client cannot access them. They also commit to using calm tone in all communication.

Coping Skills and De-Escalation

Something that makes me feel calm: Taking a bath

Somewhere I can go to feel safe: My bedroom

Music or other media that helps me: Taylor Swift

My skills: Deep breathing, journaling, calling my grandmother, playing with my dog

Safe People

People I can call: Grandma, coach, friends

People in my home I can talk to: I'm not sure about talking to my parents.

A hotline I can reach out to: Youth In Crisis – ConnectSafely 877–968–8491 (call) 839836 (text)

Worst-Case Scenario

How I will know it's worst-case scenario: If I think of another way to hurt myself

How my guardian will know: They will check in with me.

What we will do: We will go to [Hospital].

If I need more support: We will go to [Hospital].

Communication Plan

My guardian will check in on me this often: Twice a day

They will check in on me by: Telling me it's okay I'm struggling and ask how I am

I will check in with them this often: Just when I need to

I will check in by: Telling them how I feel

My next contact with my therapist: [Session date/time]

Preventative Steps

What is my plan to avoid my triggers (or respond if they come up), communicate about my needs, and take steps if I am not safe? My parents will use calm tones. I can remind them if they forget. I can ask to take a break, and my parents will let me. I can stay in my room. I will use my skills.

Sample Safety Plan (Blank)

Participants

____

____

Specific Risks

O Self-Harm O Suicide O Dangerous Behavior O Harm to Others O Risk for Abuse

Protective Factors

O Supportive people: ________________

O Something I'm looking forward to: ________________

O A goal I have: ________________

O Something important to me: ________________

Potential Triggers

____

____

____

Risk Factors

O Specific plan or ideation O Accessible means O History (This has happened before.)

O Impulse control O Lack of support O Triggers

More information: ________________

____

Coping Skills and De-Escalation

Something that makes me feel calm: ________________

Somewhere I can go to feel safe: ________________

Music or other media that helps me: ________________

My skills: ________________

____

____

Safe People

People I can call: __________

People in my home I can talk to: __________

A hotline I can reach out to: __________

Worst-Case Scenario

How I will know it's worst-case scenario: __________

How my guardian will know: __________

What we will do: __________

If I need more support: __________

Communication Plan

My guardian will check in on me this often: __________

They will check in on me by: __________

I will check in with them this often: __________

I will check in by: __________

My next contact with my therapist: __________

Preventative Steps

What is my plan to avoid my triggers (or respond if they come up), communicate about my needs, and take steps if I am not safe? __________

Glossary of Terms

harm reduction: Strategies aimed at minimizing negative outcomes from a behavior, often associated with substance use but applicable to self-harm.
hospitalization: Admission to a department of the hospital for inpatient treatment.
ideation: Thoughts or ideas about something.
intent: Resolve or decision to do something.
involuntary hospitalization: When an individual is ordered, usually by a court, to receive inpatient treatment even if they do not consent.
mandated reporting: When individuals in certain professions are required by law to disclose allegations or suspicion of harm, including child abuse or neglect.
means: Having the ability or resources to do something.
plan: Specific details for how one will do something.
risk assessment: Process by which one evaluates risks to safety or security through a series of questions and inquiries.
safety contract: An agreement between a provider and client in which the client agrees not to engage in an unsafe behavior.
safety plan: A set of techniques, tools, and steps a client will take to remain safe, which includes input from them about their goals.
self-harm behavior: A behavior in which a person injures themselves intentionally.
self-harm ideation: Thoughts of intentionally hurting oneself.
self-harm intent: Decision to cause intentional harm to oneself.
suicidal ideation: Thoughts of injuring oneself intentionally with the intent to cause death.
suicidal intent: Decision to cause one's own death.
trauma-informed: An approach to any aspect of care that assumes that any given client may have trauma history and takes steps to mitigate re-traumatization in the treatment process.

Works Cited

Child Welfare Information Gateway. (2019). *Mandatory reporters of child abuse and neglect.* US Department of Health and Human Services. www.childwelfare.gov/pubpdfs/manda.pdf

Clarke, S., Allerhand, L. A., & Berk, M. S. (2019). Recent advances in understanding and managing self-harm in adolescents. *F1000Research, 8,* 1794. https://doi.org/10.12688/f1000research.19868.1

Dazzi, T., Gribble, R., Wessely, S., & Fear, N. T. (2014). Does asking about suicide and related behaviours induce suicidal ideation? What is the evidence? *Psychological Medicine, 44*(16), 3361–3363. https://doi.org/10.1017/S0033291714001299

Garvey, K. A., Penn, J. V., Campbell, A. L., Esposito-Smythers, C., & Spirito, A. (2009). Contracting for safety with patients: Clinical practice and forensic implications. *Journal of the American Academy of Psychiatry and the Law, 37*(3), 363–370. PMID: 19767501.

Leach, M. J. (2005). Rapport: A key to treatment success. *Complementary Therapies in Clinical Practice, 11*(4), 262–265. https://doi.org/10.1016/j.ctcp.2005.05.005

Levengood, T. W., Yoon, G. H., Davoust, M. J., Ogden, S. N., Marshall, B. D. L., Cahill, S. R., & Bazzi, A. R. (2021). Supervised injection facilities as harm reduction: A systematic review. *American Journal of Preventive Medicine, 61*(5), 738–749. https://doi.org/10.1016/j.amepre.2021.04.017

Tarasoff v. Regents of the University of California, 17 Cal.3d 425, 131 Cal. Rptr. 14, 551 P. 2d 334. (1976). www.casebriefs.com/blog/law/torts/torts-keyed-to-dobbs/the-duty-to-protct-third-persons/tarasoff-v-regents-of-univesity-of-california

CHAPTER 11

LETTERS

Clients may request letters for a variety of reasons: To verify compliance with treatment, to excuse an absence from work or school, or to request accommodations. It can be challenging to comply with these requests while protecting confidentiality, and some providers struggle with knowing what to include, what to leave out, and when to agree or decline to write a letter. This chapter can help you determine when a letter is appropriate and include necessary information while protecting client privacy.

Writing Letters for Clients

Parents and legal guardians often request that a therapist provide documentation in the form of a letter. Letters can provide verification of services without having to release a detailed treatment summary or progress notes containing confidential session details.

If you work for a clinic or other organization, always check your employer's policies before agreeing to write a letter. Additionally consider any local laws or regulations, relevant ethics codes, and your scope of practice.

If you are a practicum student, intern, or other unlicensed provider practicing under your supervisor's license, any letter that you release should have both your signature and your supervisor's signature. Your supervisor will likely have feedback about how letters should be worded, what they want included, and things they avoid commenting on. Always defer to your supervisor and ask questions as needed.

Consent

If a legal guardian requests a letter for a third party who is not another of the client's legal guardians, it is important to get a written release of information authorizing you to write the letter. If the client has two legal guardians who are not married (for example, divorced parents who share 50/50 custody), best practice is to get both guardians' signatures on the consent. However, always double check your jurisdiction's requirements, as this can vary.

Another consideration is your jurisdiction's age of medical consent. In some states, clients under age 18 can provide consent for their medical treatment or for records to be released without the parent's consent. In others, they might be required to provide consent in addition to the parent's consent.

While the parent or guardian is responsible for providing legal consent to release in most cases, if they are requesting a letter addressed to them, written consent may not be necessary. For example, if a parent wants a list of the dates sessions occurred for their own records, you can typically write and release this letter without written consent, just like you do not need written consent to send someone their own bill.

DOI: 10.4324/9781003316442-11

Always consult your malpractice insurance, attorney, and local laws to ensure you are in compliance around consent.

Confidentiality

As discussed in previous chapters of this book, confidentiality can sometimes get difficult when working with children and adolescents. When a guardian requests a letter, consider the impact on your client's confidentiality and their rapport with you. For something simple, like a letter confirming an appointment time so that the client is excused from school, this may be a small issue. However, for requests including information about things like diagnosis and treatment history, this could mean that you are releasing extensive information that the client has told you privately.

Good practice, when possible, can include having a conversation with your client at their appointment. You can either draft the letter prior to the appointment or write it as a part of your session so that the client is aware of all information included, has the option to ask that you redact things that need to be kept confidential, or can ask questions about the letter.

Recommendations

While this will not always be the case, letter requests often include requests for specific recommendations about a client's care outside of their work with their therapist or another aspect of their life. When writing recommendations, we must again ensure that we are speaking within our scope of practice and using our professional judgment, as these are official recommendations.

If, for example, the letter will be presented in a child custody case and you are not qualified to make a custody recommendation (or you are not able to make a recommendation in your role as the child's therapist), you might still complete a letter but need to note the limitations on what you can recommend. You might indicate that the information provided is based on clinical observations and *not* an official recommendation.

Accommodations Letters

If you complete evaluations or assessments, you are more likely to receive requests for accommodation letters, but clients might ask therapists who do not do evaluations for accommodation letters sometimes as well. As always, defer to your scope of practice when choosing whether or not to accept these requests.

If you are able to write an accommodation letter, first ask your client specifically what they need. For things like extended time for standardized tests, the companies that administer these tests require a specific form that you complete. However, you can also provide a letter supplementing the form detailing the client's limitations, disability, and needed accommodations.

While there are many different accommodations available based on an individual's diagnosis and disability status, two people with the same diagnosis might need different accommodations. For instance, someone with Attention-Deficit/Hyperactivity Disorder might request to take a test in a separate room because they feel distracted when surrounded by other test-takers. Someone else might prefer to test around their peers because being alone is more distracting. This is why it is important to talk to your client and ask them what specific accommodations they as an individual find beneficial.

If you use a standard accommodations template with general recommendations for each client, your letter may cause more issues than it solves. Sometimes, schools or organizations will try to closely follow the accommodations listed even when they are not a good fit for the individual. In the previous example, you might recommend a separate room for testing for a client who does not benefit from that environment.

Keep track of what accommodations are appropriate for various diagnoses and presentations, and individualize your letter based on what the client needs. These letters are best written collaboratively.

Good Faith Estimates

In January 2022, the United States enacted the No Surprises Act to help mitigate the impact of medical debt by requiring providers to give uninsured or cash-pay clients a Good Faith Estimate including information about the estimated cost of their care (*Ending Surprise Medical Bills*, n.d.). Many therapists already posted information about their out-of-pocket rates on their websites, and the No Surprises Act was primarily passed to ensure that clients were not shocked by a six-figure bill following a hospital stay. However, mental health providers still need to provide Good Faith Estimates to clients who are not using their insurance, and it can be helpful to provide such estimates for clients using insurance with information about what services will cost if the claim is denied or the client's plan does not cover mental health services.

Although either the provider or the client can contact the client's insurance company prior to the start of services and ask about coverage for specific services and billing codes (specific information about billing codes is discussed in Chapter 3), representatives for the company will remind you that "Confirmation of coverage is not a guarantee of payment." In other words, they can promise to cover a service and then deny the claim after you provide the service. Additionally, if the cost of care goes to the client's deductible, the rate will be based on the specific plan's negotiated rate, which will typically be lower than the provider's cash rate. Basically, neither the client nor the provider knows for sure what a client using their insurance will owe for services until after the services are billed.

In addition, although the Paul Wellstone and Pete Domenici Mental Health Parity and Addiction Equity Act of 2008 indicates that insurance plans in the United States must offer mental health coverage that is comparable to their medical coverage (*The Mental Health Parity and Addiction Equity Act (MHPAEA), n.d.*), and although the Affordable Care Act (ACA) of 2013 requires that mental health treatment be considered "essential health benefits" to be covered by all insurance plans (*Affordable care act expands mental health and substance use disorder benefits and federal parity protections for 62 million Americans, n.d.*), this often does not pan out in practice. The ACA was enacted in 2013, and by 2014, United Behavioral Health (UBH) was subject to a class action lawsuit because they had violated this requirement by refusing to cover mental health services for more than 60,000 claims.

In *Wit vs UBH*, a judge initially determined that the insurance company was in violation of the ACA by denying these claims. However, in January 2023, a panel of three judges overturned this ruling, indicating that UBH did not have to pay the claims (*Wit vs UBH*, 2023). Essentially, this case set a precedent for clients' out-of-pocket costs for mental health care to skyrocket.

Still, although we might not know what a client's eventual out-of-pocket costs might be, the provider can offer a "worst-case scenario" estimate detailing what the client will owe if insurance fully denies the claim. This can be based on the provider's cash rate, which is typically higher than the negotiated rate. A Good Faith Estimate cannot underestimate the cost of treatment, but it is acceptable for treatment to cost less than what is indicated on the Good Faith Estimate. Essentially, it is better to estimate too high and then let your client know that their care will actually cost less than anticipated than to estimate too low and go over the amount. In fact, clients can contest a bill if it is more than $400 higher than the Good Faith Estimate (*Ending Surprise Medical Bills*, n.d.).

The Good Faith Estimate includes information about what services will be provided and the total cost of services. It can be challenging in therapy to make these estimates, as we typically do not know exactly how many sessions a client will need or want. One way to address this is to generate a new Good Faith Estimate on a regular basis and indicate this on the form. For example, you might calculate what weekly sessions for six months will cost and note that the estimate is for six months of therapy, to be re-evaluated at that time. Since it is good practice to review treatment plans regularly (as we discussed in Chapter 6), a new Good Faith Estimate can be part of the treatment plan review.

Emotional Support Animals

An emotional support animal, according to the Americans With Disabilities Network, is "any animal that provides emotional support alleviating one or more symptoms of a person's disability" (*Service animal or emotional support animal: What's the difference?*, 2023). Unlike service animals, emotional support animals are not trained to perform a specific task, and they are not permitted in public spaces that do not allow pets. However, a disabled person who lives in pet-free housing can keep an emotional support animal who helps them with their disability. Additionally, landlords cannot charge pet rent or pet deposits for emotional support animals.

Unfortunately, there are not current set, specific standards for who needs an emotional support animal, who does not, and what psychological assessment tools are the standard for making this determination, and many providers and boards have brought up ethical concerns about the practice of writing these letters (Fine et al., 2019). Concerns include the specific role of the emotional support animal and possible liability to the therapist if they write this letter and the animal damages the living space.

If it is within your scope of practice to determine whether or not someone qualifies for an emotional support animal, you can include a caveat in the letter that you and your client (or their legal guardian) have discussed potential risks for having an emotional support animal. While landlords cannot charge pet rent for an emotional support animal, they can charge for damage the animal does to the property – your emotional support cat does not have a pet fee, but if the cat tears up the carpet, you may have to cover the cost to fix it.

Similarly, since emotional support animals do not have any specific training they need to complete, some worry that they will be liable for misbehavior. After all, if your emotional support dog attacks someone, you are liable just like you would be for an ordinary pet dog.

Another factor to consider is that, unlike medical equipment or other accommodations, emotional support animals are living beings with their own needs. If a client is unable financially or physically to provide the animal with the care they need, an emotional support animal is not an appropriate accommodation.

If you document that you and your client discussed this and that they understand it is their liability and not yours, you might still choose to write these letters. After all, emotional support animals can benefit people with mental health issues: Someone who struggles to get out of bed due to depression might get up because their dog needs to go out to use the bathroom. Someone who forgets to eat due to executive dysfunction or dissociation will remember to feed themselves when their animal cues them that it is dinner time.

As always, it is up to each therapist to get and maintain education about best practices, laws, and ethics if they choose to offer this service.

Service Animals

Unlike emotional support animals, service animals perform at least one specific task that helps a disabled individual function. According to the Americans With Disabilities Act, only dogs are recognized as service animals according to Title II and Title III, though there are some exceptions for miniature horses (*ADA Requirements: Service Animals*, 2023). A physically disabled person with a service animal may also have mental health difficulties, and some service animals are trained specifically to help with mental health issues. For example, service dogs can learn to help calm an individual down during a panic attack or PTSD flashback. They can also provide deep pressure and sensory support to an autistic person.

Service animals are permitted in "state and local governments, businesses, and nonprofit organizations that serve the public . . . in all areas of the facility where the public is allowed to go." Service animals are required to be trained and under control, and businesses can ask a handler and their service animal to leave if the animal is not under control. Service animal training usually includes training to ensure that the animal will remain under control in public spaces (*ADA Requirements: Service Animals*, 2023).

While service animals must be properly trained, they do not have to complete a specific training or even use a professional trainer, so individuals who have the skills to train their service animal can do so on their own. However, service animals in training are not covered under the ADA, so the individual will have to complete the training in full before they are guaranteed entrance in public spaces (*Frequently asked questions about service animals and the ADA*, 2023).

Clients may sometimes ask for a letter documenting need for a service animal, indicating that it is a "legitimate" service animal. However, "Mandatory registration of service animals is not permissible under the ADA" (*Frequently asked questions about service animals and the ADA*, 2023). There is no registry of service animals, therapists cannot certify or register a service animal, and businesses cannot request registration or documentation of the type of disability. Under the ADA rules around service animals, therapists should not write letters for service animals.

When to Say No

There may be times when a client requests a letter that you do not feel comfortable providing or asks you to offer a recommendation that is outside your scope of practice. In this case, you can document the contact, the request, and your reason for declining in a contact note (Chapter 9).

If, for example, a client requests a letter for an emotional support animal in pet-free housing, and you are not trained in determining whether or not an emotional support animal is appropriate for them, it would not be appropriate to provide a letter making this recommendation.

Parents who are divorced or in the process of getting divorced might request a letter with custody recommendations. Typically, if you are the primary therapist, you cannot make a recommendation regarding custody even if you are ordinarily qualified to make these kinds of recommendations. As the client's primary therapist, you are not a neutral party doing a custody evaluation or recommendation.

A guardian might indicate that they understand that you cannot make a custody recommendation and still request a letter confirming that the client is in therapy. You might decide that this is appropriate; in this case, it is important to note these limitations in the letter. The judge or one party's lawyer might subpoena you to testify and, once on the stand, ask you to make a custody recommendation. We have an ethical responsibility to tell the judge that such a recommendation is outside of our scope if this is the case, and documenting this limitation early on can save all parties time and resources.

When navigating requests for letters regarding custody battles, if the parents have joint custody, best practice is to release any records, documentation, or letters to both parents or their legal representation simultaneously. The parents are not your clients, and it is important to maintain neutrality and not favor either parent.

Samples

On the following pages, I have provided samples of various types of letters I am often asked to write. This includes documentation to excuse an absence, confirmation of the client's diagnosis, verifying dates of sessions, and accommodations requests. The letters do not have specific templates, but you can easily take the wording and create your own letter with your client's information inserted. I have also included templates for Good Faith Estimates for cost of services.

Please note: For accommodation letters, there is not a sample form because each company requires their own specific form. A sample emotional support animal letter is also not included because there are not presently set standards for what should or should not be included in these assessments. Instead, those who choose to offer this service can use the tips presented in the chapter as guidance if needed.

Sample Letter: School Absence

[Date]

Re: Appointment

To Whom It May Concern:

I am writing with regard to [Client] at the request of their guardian. [Client] had an appointment with me on [date] at [time]. Please excuse this absence. Thank you.

Sincerely,

[Your name and credentials]

Sample Letter: Confirmation of Diagnosis

[Date]

Dear [Guardian]:

I am writing this letter at your request regarding [Client]. [Client] is aware that I am writing this letter for you. You initially contacted me because [Client] [brief description of presenting problem], and I completed an intake interview on [Date]. I have since had [note number of sessions, who was present, etc.].

Based on [review of Client's symptoms], I have diagnosed [Client] with [Diagnosis].

Children with [Diagnosis] [this can be re-worded as identity-first language when appropriate] present with [note symptoms of Diagnosis]. For [Client], this manifests as [details about Client's presentation].

Please do not hesitate to contact me with any questions or concerns.

Sincerely,

[Your name and credentials]

Sample Letter: Confirmation of Services for Court

[Date]

[Contact information for Judge]

Re: [Client name and date of birth]

Dear [Judge]:

I am writing with regard to [Client]. Per an order you signed on [Date], [Client] is mandated to attend [details about court ordered treatment]. This letter serves as an update regarding [Guardian]'s compliance with this order.

[Note here dates of sessions Client attended, missed, cancelled, or rescheduled appointments and reasons given.]

[*Only* if required by the order, include any essential additional information regarding treatment progression.]

If you have any further questions or concerns about this letter, please do not hesitate to contact me.

Respectfully,

[Your name and credentials]

Sample Letter: Court-Ordered Treatment Summary

[Date]

[Court contact information]

Re: [Client name and date of birth]

Dear [Judge]:

Per your signed order dated [Date], I am providing a summary regarding my treatment with [Client]. [Note: If the summary is not mandated but was requested by the guardian, and you have appropriate consent, note here that the report is written at the guardian's request and with their authorization. In that case, note also that the summary is provided to both parties' attorneys, if applicable.] At [Client's] last appointment, we spoke about this summary.

This letter includes a summary of [Client]'s presenting symptoms, history, and treatment so far.

[Parent 1] presented for an intake to provide [Client's] background and presenting concerns on [Date]. [Parent 2] met with me on [Date] to provide additional context and background information. Due to the high-conflict nature of [Parent 1] and [Parent 2]'s relationship at this time, it is my professional opinion that separate meetings would be most beneficial for furnishing me with a thorough history for [Client]. Information that I have about [Client's] history is based on the information provided by [Parent 1] and [Parent 2].

Since this time, [Client] has attended six individual therapy sessions with me. My clinical observations of [Client's] symptoms is based on my observations during these sessions and information [Client] has shared with me about their symptoms outside of the session environment.

Both parents indicted that they presently share 50/50 custody of [Client] with a week-on, week-off schedule, and this has been the arrangement for one year. [Parent 1] stated that [Client] becomes anxious to the point of tearful one to two days prior to transitioning to [Parent 2's] house, stating that she does not want to go and wants to stay with [Parent 1]. [Parent 1] states that she is requesting a change in the custody schedule because these symptoms have reportedly increased in severity over time. [Parent 1] denied that [Client] has alleged abuse in [Parent 2's] home but has stated that [Parent 2] does not play with her or spend time with her, and [Parent 1] stated that [Client] often returns from [Parent 2's] house with incomplete homework assignments.

[Parent 2] stated that [Client] presents as happy to see him when he picks her up from school on the transition days. He stated that [Client] is often very tired after school and does not want to do her homework, but he believes this is developmentally appropriate. He stated that [Client] is in charge of completing her assignments because he wants her to learn responsibility around this. [Parent 2] stated that he has not observed anxiety symptoms in [Client] around transitions or at any other time.

When meeting with me, [Client] verified becoming anxious in the days before transitions. She stated that she becomes tearful when at [Parent 1's] house, but at [Parent 2's] house she does not outwardly express this because "[Parent 2] doesn't understand." [Client] denied abuse or neglect in either home but stated that she does not like changing houses every week because she is afraid that she will "forget something" at one house. She stated that because [Parent 1] and [Parent 2] "hate each other," she cannot ask them to pick something up if she forgets. She shared that she has forgotten preferred clothes and toys as well as school supplies when changing houses. She stated that she feels "like I'm always packing to go somewhere, and I can't relax."

[Client] presents for her sessions as engaged and talkative, and she enjoys playing various board games while discussing things with me. She talks openly about her experiences in both homes and typically appears happy. Her mental status is consistent on weeks with [Parent 1] and [Parent 2].

The information provided is limited to what I am told by [Client], [Parent 1], and [Parent 2], as well as my clinical observations during [Client's] sessions. It is not within my role as a therapist to investigate evidence or weigh veracity of truth, nor is it within the bounds of my work with [Client] to conduct a custody evaluation or provide a recommendation for custody. My professional opinions about [Client's] mental health and treatment are based on the information provided to me.

If you have any questions or concerns about this letter, please do not hesitate to contact me.

Respectfully,

[Your name and credentials]

Sample Letter: Confirmation of Session Dates

[Date]

Re: [Client name and date of birth]

Dear [Parent/guardian or parents]:

Per [Parent's] request, I have put together a list of session dates for [Client]. Her regular appointment time is Monday at 4:00 p.m., and she presently attends weekly sessions with me. I also noted the reason given for cancellations.

February

- 12: Appointment kept
- 19: Appointment kept
- 26: Cancelled due to therapist illness

March

- 4: Appointment kept
- 11: Appointment kept
- 18: Cancelled for school activity
- 25: Appointment kept

April

- 1: Appointment kept
- 8: Appointment kept
- 15: Appointment kept
- 22: Appointment kept
- 29: Appointment kept

May

- 6: Cancelled due to client illness
- 13: Appointment kept
- 20: Appointment kept
- 27: Cancelled for Memorial Day holiday

June

- 3: Appointment kept
- 10: Appointment kept

For cancellations made by a parent, I was notified [Client] would not attend as far in advance as possible.

If you have any questions or concerns about this letter, please do not hesitate to contact me.

Respectfully,

[Your name and credentials]

Sample Letter: Accommodations Request

[Date]

Re: [Client name and date of birth]

Dear [Requesting Party]:

I am writing this letter with regard to [Client]. I have received written consent from [Client's] parents and verbal assent from [Client] to write this letter. My understanding is that this letter will be used in developing [Client's] 504 plan with [School].

[Note any information about diagnostic assessments, testing, et cetera completed]. Based on this, results indicated [Note relevant results]. Per this information, [Client] meets the *Diagnostic and Statistical Manual of Mental Disorders* criteria for [Diagnosis]. Children with [Diagnosis] are entitled to academic accommodations under [State] laws and the Americans With Disabilities Act.

[If you have spoken with your client about what specific accommodations will benefit them and confirmed that those accommodations are appropriate based on their diagnosis, you can list those recommendations here. Otherwise, you can leave out recommendations and defer to the school and guardians as they develop the 504 plan.]

If you have any questions about this letter or about [Client's] diagnosis, please do not hesitate to contact me.

Sincerely,

[Your name and credentials]

Sample Good Faith Estimate for Therapy

Date of Estimate: ________ /________ /________

Provider Information

Provider Name: ________________________ Provider Type: ________________________

Address: ________________________ City: ____________ State: ________ Zip:__________

Phone Number: ________________________ Email: ________________________________

National Provider Identifier: __________________ Taxpayer Identification Number: ______________

Client Information

Client: ____

First *Middle* *Last*

Date of Birth: ________ /________ /________

Address: ________________________ City: ____________ State: ________ Zip:__________

Phone Number: ________________________ Email: ________________________________

Presenting Concern

Service requested: Individual Therapy Services

Provisional Diagnosis*: F34.9 Unspecified Depressive Disorder

Secondary Diagnosis (if applicable): ____

If scheduled, date the primary service will be provided: ________ /________ /________ ________ N/A

Services Requested

Billing Code 1: 90791 Estimated Units: 1 Cost Per Unit: $150

Explanation: Intake and diagnostic interview to gather a thorough history and information about presenting symptoms

Billing Code 2: 90834 Estimated Units: 24 Cost Per Unit: $100

Explanation: Therapy sessions lasting 45 minutes each, weekly for six months

Billing Code 3: ____________ Estimated Units: ________ Cost Per Unit: ________

Explanation: ____

____

____

Billing Code 4: ____________ Estimated Units: ________ Cost Per Unit: ________

Explanation: ____

____

____

Billing Code 5: ____________ Estimated Units: ________ Cost Per Unit: ________

Explanation: ____

____

____

Total Estimated Cost for Service: $2,550

The estimated cost is valid for 12 months from the date of this Good Faith Estimate.

* The provisional diagnosis is based on symptom information provided by the client. It is not a medical diagnosis or official part of the client's medical record. This diagnosis will be updated as appropriate after the start of treatment.

Your signature below indicates understanding of the Good Faith Estimate and agreement to pay the amount indicated in the estimate. Should your total cost of services be less than the Good Faith Estimate, you will only be expected to pay the cost of services and not the full Good Faith Estimate. If you have any questions or concerns, or you are uncomfortable signing the Good Faith Estimate, please contact me.

Client Name (print): ____________________ Date: ____________________

Legal Guardian (if applicable): ________________ Relationship: ________________

Client/Guardian Signature: ______________________________________

Disclaimer

This Good Faith Estimate shows the costs of items and services that are reasonably expected for your healthcare needs for an item or service. The estimate is based on information known at the time the estimate was created.

The Good Faith Estimate does not include any unknown or unexpected costs that may arise during treatment. You could be charged more if complications or special circumstances occur. If this happens, federal law allows you to dispute (appeal) the bill.

If you are billed for more than this Good Faith Estimate, you have the right to dispute the bill.

You may contact the healthcare provider or facility listed to let them know the billed charges are higher than the Good Faith Estimate. You can ask them to update the bill to match the Good Faith Estimate, ask to negotiate the bill, or ask whether there is financial assistance available.

You may also start a dispute resolution process with the U.S. Department of Health and Human Services (HHS). If you choose to use the dispute resolution process, you must start the dispute process within 120 calendar days (about 4 months) of the date on the original bill.

There is a $25 fee to use the dispute process. If the agency reviewing your dispute agrees with you, you will have to pay the price on this Good Faith Estimate. If the agency disagrees with you and agrees with the healthcare provider or facility, you will have to pay the higher amount.

To learn more and get a form to start the process, go to www.cms.gov/nosurprises or call 1-800-985-3059.

For questions or more information about your right to a Good Faith Estimate or the dispute process, visit www.cms.gov/nosurprises or call 1-800-985-3059.

Keep a copy of this Good Faith Estimate or take pictures of it. You will need it if you are billed a higher amount and choose to dispute the bill.

Sample Good Faith Estimate for Therapy (Blank)

Date of Estimate: ________ /________ /________

Provider Information

Provider Name: ______________________________ Provider Type: ______________________________

Address: ______________________ City: ____________ State: ________ Zip:__________

Phone Number: __________________________ Email: ______________________________

National Provider Identifier: ________________ Taxpayer Identification Number: ____________

Client Information

Client: ____

First *Middle* *Last*

Date of Birth: ________ /________ /________

Address: ______________________ City: ____________ State: ________ Zip:__________

Phone Number: ______________________ Email: ______________________________

Presenting Concern

Service requested: ____

Provisional Diagnosis*: ____

Secondary Diagnosis (if applicable): ____

If scheduled, date the primary service will be provided: ________ /________ /________ ________ N/A

Services Requested

Billing Code 1: __________________ Estimated Units: ____________ Cost Per Unit: ____________

Explanation: ____

____

____

Billing Code 2: __________________ Estimated Units: ____________ Cost Per Unit: ____________

Explanation: ____

____

____

Billing Code 3: ____________ Estimated Units: ________ Cost Per Unit: ________

Explanation: ____

____

____

Billing Code 4: ____________ Estimated Units: ________ Cost Per Unit: ________

Explanation: ____

____

____

Billing Code 5: ____________ Estimated Units: ________ Cost Per Unit: ________

Explanation: ____

____

____

Total Estimated Cost for Service

The estimated cost is valid for 12 months from the date of this Good Faith Estimate.

* The provisional diagnosis is based on symptom information provided by the client. It is not a medical diagnosis or official part of the client's medical record. This diagnosis will be updated as appropriate after the start of treatment.

Your signature below indicates understanding of the Good Faith Estimate and agreement to pay the amount indicated in the estimate. Should your total cost of services be less than the Good Faith Estimate, you will only be expected to pay the cost of services and not the full Good Faith Estimate. If you have any questions or concerns, or you are uncomfortable signing the Good Faith Estimate, please contact me.

Client Name (print): ____________________ Date: ____________________

Legal Guardian (if applicable): ____________________ Relationship: ____________________

Client/Guardian Signature: ____

Disclaimer

This Good Faith Estimate shows the costs of items and services that are reasonably expected for your healthcare needs for an item or service. The estimate is based on information known at the time the estimate was created.

The Good Faith Estimate does not include any unknown or unexpected costs that may arise during treatment. You could be charged more if complications or special circumstances occur. If this happens, federal law allows you to dispute (appeal) the bill.

If you are billed for more than this Good Faith Estimate, you have the right to dispute the bill.

You may contact the healthcare provider or facility listed to let them know the billed charges are higher than the Good Faith Estimate. You can ask them to update the bill to match the Good Faith Estimate, ask to negotiate the bill, or ask whether there is financial assistance available.

You may also start a dispute resolution process with the U.S. Department of Health and Human Services (HHS). If you choose to use the dispute resolution process, you must start the dispute process within 120 calendar days (about 4 months) of the date on the original bill.

There is a $25 fee to use the dispute process. If the agency reviewing your dispute agrees with you, you will have to pay the price on this Good Faith Estimate. If the agency disagrees with you and agrees with the healthcare provider or facility, you will have to pay the higher amount.

To learn more and get a form to start the process, go to www.cms.gov/nosurprises or call 1-800-985-3059.

For questions or more information about your right to a Good Faith Estimate or the dispute process, visit www.cms.gov/nosurprises or call 1-800-985-3059.

Keep a copy of this Good Faith Estimate or take pictures of it. You will need it if you are billed a higher amount and choose to dispute the bill.

Sample Good Faith Estimate for Psychological Evaluations

Date of Estimate: ________ /________ /________

Provider Information

Provider Name: ______________________________ Provider Type: ______________________________

Address: ______________________ City: ____________ State: ________ Zip:__________

Phone Number: ______________________________ Email: ______________________________

National Provider Identifier: ________________ Taxpayer Identification Number: ______________

Client Information

Client: ____

First *Middle* *Last*

Date of Birth: ________ /________ /________

Address: ______________________ City: ____________ State: ________ Zip:__________

Phone Number: ______________________ Email: ______________________________

Presenting Concern

Service requested: ____

Provisional Diagnosis*: F41.9 Unspecified Anxiety Disorder

Secondary Diagnosis (if applicable): Rule-Out for ADHD

If scheduled, date the primary service will be provided: ________ /________ /________ ________ N/A

Services Requested

Billing Code 1: 90791 Estimated Units: 1 Cost Per Unit: $250

Explanation: Intake appointment for history and symptoms

____

____

Billing Code 2: 96136 Estimated Units: 1 Cost Per Unit: $112.50

Explanation: Administration of assessment measures, first 30 minutes

Billing Code 3: 96137 Estimated Units: 2 Cost Per Unit: $112.50

Explanation: Administration of assessment measures, additional 30 minutes per unit

Billing Code 4: 96130 Estimated Units: 1 Cost Per Unit: $225

Explanation: Evaluation interpretation and report writing, first hour

Billing Code 5: 96131 Estimated Units: 1 Cost Per Unit: $225

Explanation: Evaluation and interpretation report writing, subsequent hour

Billing Code 6: 90834 Estimated Units: 1 Cost Per Unit: $155

Explanation: 45-minute session to review test results and answer questions about the report

Total Estimated Cost for Service: $1,192.50

The estimated cost is valid for 12 months from the date of this Good Faith Estimate.

* The provisional diagnosis is based on symptom information provided by the client. It is not a medical diagnosis or official part of the client's medical record. This diagnosis will be updated as appropriate after the start of treatment.

Your signature below indicates understanding of the Good Faith Estimate and agreement to pay the amount indicated in the estimate. Should your total cost of services be less than the Good Faith Estimate, you will only be expected to pay the cost of services and not the full Good Faith Estimate. If you have any questions or concerns, or you are uncomfortable signing the Good Faith Estimate, please contact me.

Client Name (print): ______________________ Date: ______________________

Legal Guardian (if applicable): ______________________ Relationship: ______________________

Client/Guardian Signature: ____

Disclaimer

This Good Faith Estimate shows the costs of items and services that are reasonably expected for your healthcare needs for an item or service. The estimate is based on information known at the time the estimate was created.

The Good Faith Estimate does not include any unknown or unexpected costs that may arise during treatment. You could be charged more if complications or special circumstances occur. If this happens, federal law allows you to dispute (appeal) the bill.

If you are billed for more than this Good Faith Estimate, you have the right to dispute the bill.

You may contact the healthcare provider or facility listed to let them know the billed charges are higher than the Good Faith Estimate. You can ask them to update the bill to match the Good Faith Estimate, ask to negotiate the bill, or ask whether there is financial assistance available.

You may also start a dispute resolution process with the U.S. Department of Health and Human Services (HHS). If you choose to use the dispute resolution process, you must start the dispute process within 120 calendar days (about 4 months) of the date on the original bill.

There is a $25 fee to use the dispute process. If the agency reviewing your dispute agrees with you, you will have to pay the price on this Good Faith Estimate. If the agency disagrees with you and agrees with the healthcare provider or facility, you will have to pay the higher amount.

To learn more and get a form to start the process, go to www.cms.gov/nosurprises or call 1-800-985-3059.

For questions or more information about your right to a Good Faith Estimate or the dispute process, visit www.cms.gov/nosurprises or call 1-800-985-3059.

Keep a copy of this Good Faith Estimate or take pictures of it. You will need it if you are billed a higher amount and choose to dispute the bill.

Glossary of Terms

accommodations: An environmental modification or adjustment to provide accessibility to disabled individuals in school, work, and other settings.

Emotional Support Animal (ESA): An animal who provides emotional or psychological support to a disabled individual. Emotional Support Animals do not perform a task or function like service animals, but they are permitted to live in pet-free housing in the United States.

Good Faith Estimate: In healthcare, a document which details expected services and their cost.

No Surprises Act: A law protecting people from unexpected medical bills which requires providers to create an estimate of the cost of services prior to billing when the client is uninsured or not using insurance to pay for their care.

Service Animal: Under the Americans With Disabilities Act, Service Animals are dogs that are trained in and assist with performing at least one specific task for a disabled individual.

Works Cited

ADA requirements: Service animals. (2023, February 9). *ADA.gov*. Retrieved February 10, 2023, from www.ada.gov/resources/service-animals-2010-requirements/

Affordable care act expands mental health and substance use disorder benefits and federal parity protections for 62 million Americans. (n.d.). *ASPE*. Retrieved February 10, 2023, from https://aspe.hhs.gov/reports/affordable-care-act-expands-mental-health-substance-use-disorder-benefits-federal-parity-protections-0

Ending surprise medical bills. (n.d.). *CMS*. Retrieved February 10, 2023, from www.cms.gov/nosurprises

Fine, A., Beck, A., & Ng, Z. (2019). The state of animal-assisted interventions: Addressing the contemporary issues that will shape the future. *International Journal of Environmental Research and Public Health, 16*(20), 3997. https://doi.org/10.3390/ijerph16203997

Frequently asked questions about service animals and the ADA. (2023, February 9). *ADA.gov*. Retrieved February 10, 2023, from www.ada.gov/resources/service-animals-faqs/

The mental health parity and addiction equity act (MHPAEA). (n.d.). *CMS*. Retrieved February 10, 2023, from www.cms.gov/CCIIO/Programs-and-Initiatives/Other-Insurance-Protections/mhpaea_factsheet

Service animal or emotional support animal: What's the difference? (2023, February 10). *ADA National Network*. Retrieved February 10, 2023, from https://adata.org/service-animal-resource-hub/differences

Wit vs. UBH. Case No. 14-cv-02346-JCS (N.D. Cal). (2023, January 26).

INDEX

Made in the USA
Coppell, TX
01 August 2024

35408606R00116